THE TRUE NATURE OF THE
CAT

THE TRUE NATURE OF THE
CAT

DR JOHN BRADSHAW

BXTREE

The hardcover edition was first published in Great Britain in 1993 by Boxtree Limited, Broadwall House, 21 Broadwall, London SE1 9PL

This paperback edition first published by Boxtree Limited in 1994

10 9 8 7 6 5 4 3 2 1

We would like to thank the following photographers whose work appears in the books on the pages indicated:
Adams Picture Library (photographer unknown) 183
Des and Jen Bartlet (Survival Anglia Ltd.) 10, 190
Andrew Besley (Adams Picture Library) 123
Dr Sarah Brown 159
Jane Burton (Bruce Coleman Ltd.) 15, 58, 166, 167
Stuart Church 175, 215
Paddy Cutts (Animal's Unlimited) 63, 66, 90, 115, 150, 155, 219
Marc Henrie 79, 143, 187, 199
Dr Gillian Kerby 6, 95, 106, 154, 171
Debby Smith 218
K. Wothe (Bruce Coleman Ltd.) 98

Illustrations on pages 31, 37, 134-135, 152 by Priscilla Barrett
All other illustrations by Raymond Turvey
Sonagraphs on page 158 courtesy of Dr. Jean-Luc Renck

We would like to thank the publishers of the following books and periodicals for allowing us to quote extracts:
p20 *Wild Cats of the World* CAW Guggisberg David and Charles
p60 *Daily Telegraph Magazine* (16/1/93)
p76-7 *Mind in Evolution* L T Hobhouse Macmillan & Co.
p157 *The Science and Mystery of the Cat*
I M Mellen
C Scribners Sons

Design by Hammond Hammond and Anita Ruddell
Typeset by SX Composing Ltd., Rayleigh, Essex
Printed and bound in

ISBN: 0 7522 1609 0

A CIP catalogue entry for this book is available from the British Library

ACKNOWLEDGEMENTS

Writing is a solitary task, but research is not. My understanding of cats owes a great deal to the enthusiasm and insights of numerous biologists. To anyone I have left out of this list, my apologies. At the Anthrozoology Institute where I work, Sarah Brown, Sarah Lowe, Debby Smith, Katie Durman, David Roy, Fiona Smart, Diana Sawyer, Helen Jones, Stuart Church, Steve Wickens, Debbie Goodwin, Sarah Hall, Anne McBride and Rory Putman have all contributed to our ongoing study of the cat-owner relationship. Our studies have been considerably helped by the cooperation and understanding of the Blue Cross and St Francis Animal Welfare shelters, and by Edna Abraham and her staff at Brook House Animal Hospital, who have looked after both our own pets and the feral cats that we have brought in for treatment. The Waltham Centre for Pet Nutrition, the Cats Protection League and the Universities Federation for Animal Welfare have all generously provided financial support. Gillian Kerby, Warner Passanisi and David Macdonald from Oxford University; Michael Mendl, Sandra McCune, Hilary Feldman and James Serpell from Cambridge University; Chris Thorne, Louise Healey, Ian Robinson and Helen Nott from the Waltham Centre for Pet Nutrition, and Peter Neville of the Association of Pet Behaviour Counsellors have all contributed ideas and allowed me to quote from their research. To all of these, and to all the cats who have tolerated my watching them (especially Splodge, Lucy and Calypso), thank you.

Most of all my thanks goes to my family, who have put up with my regular absences in the evenings and at weekends while I have been studying and writing about cats.

J W S Bradshaw 1993

TERMINOLOGY

The word "cat" has several different meanings; it can refer just to the domestic cat, *Felis sylvestris catus*, or to the whole cat family. In this book, the term "domestic cat" is used wherever there is any chance of confusion, but otherwise the "domestic" part is dropped for brevity. Similarly, the term "wild cat" is often used to describe all the cats, big and small, that are not domesticated. I have used "wildcat" when referring specifically to the close wild relatives of the domestic cat. Further confusion can arise because not all domestic cats are domesticated; those that have gone wild or semi-wild, but whose recent ancestors were domesticated, are referred to as "feral cats". The widespread practice of neutering (spaying or castrating) pet cats has left the reproductively intact cat a somewhat unfamiliar beast. I refer to these latter cats as "entire".

Contents

Introduction

*P*eople have been fascinated by cats ever since they were first domesticated in Egypt, thousands of years ago. Part of their appeal is their faintly mysterious nature, a look on their faces that implies that they are the *really* smart ones in the family. This book attempts to explain what it is really like to be a cat. It describes what we know about the way a cat sees, hears, and thinks about the world in which it lives, how it relates to its own kind, and what it thinks of us.

This book will not tell you how to look after your cat, but it should help you to look at your cat in a new light. Until quite recently, it was not fashionable for biologists to study domesticated animals. The information in the scientific literature became out-of-date and largely forgotten. Lately, however, there has been a surge of interest in the behaviour of cats, and they have been studied under all kinds of circumstances, from the cats that live high up in the apartments of Zurich, to those that live semi-wild on the farms of Wisconsin. Somewhere between these two extremes lie the cats of Southampton, which my students and I have been studying for the past six years. Based in the Biology Department at Southampton University, we have recently formed ourselves into the Anthrozoology Institute, an organization devoted to the study of the interactions between people and their pets. We have concentrated our attention on the puzzle of how cats came to live with us in the first place, and now that they are here, what they think of us. We still have more questions than answers, but the questions are interesting in their own right, and much of the last chapter of this book is devoted to posing them and offering some speculative solutions.

As we head towards the twenty-first century, it looks as if the cat will become our commonest household pet. It has adapted marvellously to man-made environments in the past, but new demands are being placed upon it as its traditional role of rat-catcher is usurped by agrochemicals. The more we know about cats, the more we can help them to adjust to a rapidly changing environment.

The purpose of this book is to take the information that is currently known only to biologists, and bring it to a wider audience. I have found that the more I understand about cats in general, and my own cats in particular, the more fascinating they have become. I hope this book will do the same for the reader.

CHAPTER 1

Wildcats and Free

Komani, a purebred tabby female, slips into her owner's garden as the daylight fades. He is sitting quietly on his veranda, reading. She runs to him, jumps on to his shoulder, pushes between him and his book, rubs her flank on his face, then rolls on the now dis-carded book, purring all the while. In her enthusiasm, she rolls over on his lap and in doing so nearly falls to the ground.

Many cat owners will be familiar with this elaborate ritual, even if they suspect that it may only be a preliminary to the more serious business of feeding-time. What is extraordinary about this account is that it refers not to a pampered pet in some leafy suburb, but to a fully-grown 4.5 kg (10 lb) wildcat in Africa. The owner is biologist Dr Reay Smithers of the University of Pretoria, who hand-reared both Komani and her sister Goro. Komani, Goro and others like them tell us a great deal about the relationship between cat and man, for not only are the wildcats' behaviour patterns similar to those of a domestic cat, but their genes are virtually identical. Only a few thousand years have elapsed since the domestic cat emerged as separate from the African wildcat. This is a tiny, if significant, fraction of the twelve million years it has taken for the modern cat family to evolve. By throwing in its lot with ours, domestic cats have spread to the four corners of the world. They have grown in numbers while all the other members of the cat family have dwindled away, many of them today becoming endangered species; tragically, a few of these are on the verge of extinction.

(Opposite) An African Wildcat from Namibia. The ancestors of the domestic cat must have looked very like this.

Cats are carnivores, meat-eaters. In fact, the cat family is the most committed to meat-eating of all the carnivores, and we will see in later chapters just how the domestic cat still carries all the hallmarks of a nocturnal hunter, even though today many hunt nothing more lively than a catnip mouse. To understand how this came about, we must journey back to a time when many kinds of now extinct large cats lived. These included giant sabre-tooth cats like *Smilodon*, and a still more primitive giant cat *Barbourofelis* which died out, in North America, only about seven million years ago and must have lived alongside some of the modern cats. Unfortunately we know very little about the early ancestors of today's species. They were probably small animals that lived for the most part in tropical forests, where fossils are rarely formed. It was not until about two million years ago that the current crop of large cats evolved, left the forest and began to forage on the open plain, where their remains stood a better chance of being preserved.

The lion emerged in Africa, now its stronghold once again. However, in the warm periods between the ice ages, ancestral lions (*Panthera utrox*) invaded Asia, and spread eastwards until they reached the Bering land bridge that, until 10,000 years ago, connected Asia to Alaska. Their journey continued southwards until they reached Peru in South America. Then changes in the climate, leading to a reduction in the grassland that suits lions best, drove them out of America.

The leopards probably first evolved in India, and then spread to Africa and Europe. One form of leopard, the ancestor of the modern jaguar, also migrated across the Bering land bridge. (About 25,000 years ago, the ancestors of today's North American Indians made exactly the same migration.) Probably because leopards are much more adaptable than lions, one species of jaguar still lives in Southern and Central America.

The first tigers appeared in China over two million years ago, but their spread was not so extensive as that of either lion or leopard. One branch of the tiger family spread westwards across Asia, keeping to the north of the Himalayas, and eventually reached the Caspian Sea. Another branch spread south from China into South-East Asia, then north-west into Burma and finally into India, where it now has one of its final strongholds in and around Bengal. The northern branch is now best represented by the Siberian tiger; the other populations are either extinct or nearly so.

Cheetahs, despite the racy build that allows them to be the world's fastest land mammals, are actually quite closely related to the other large cats. This has been one of the surprises provided by the application of modern molecular techniques to the study of evolution. By studying the similarities between proteins in modern species, or differences in the DNA which forms the genetic make-up of each animal, it has been possible to construct a molecular clock for the cat family. While the racy cheetah looks quite different to the more solidly-built tiger or lion, the molecular information suggests that they all had a common ancestor, perhaps about three million years ago. The earliest fossil cheetah that has been discovered is a giant, more heavily built than the modern species. It was found not in Africa, but in France, where its presence today would probably lead to panic! Cheetahs once roamed throughout India, Arabia and Africa. Fossils of cheetah-like cats have been found in America, suggesting that they may have followed the lion and leopard across the Bering land bridge. However, some biologists think that the American cheetahs evolved separately from local ancestors, and that their similarity to the African and Asian cheetahs arose because they all used the sprinting chase as their preferred hunting method. This may never be resolved, because the American cheetahs became extinct some time in the last 10,000 years.

The same fate seems to have nearly befallen the African cheetah, the sole surviving species. At about the same time as the last American cheetah disappeared, the African population crashed to a small number of individuals, which just managed to hang on and breed sufficiently for their numbers to increase again. A further population crash occurred in South Africa in the nineteenth century. The result is that in East Africa and even more so in South Africa, cheetahs are almost clones of one another. Genetically they are all virtually identical, perhaps as similar to one another as dogs of the same breed. In the population crashes much of their genetic diversity was lost for ever. This means that, today, the cheetah has less variability than other large cats (for example, about five times less than the lion has), and should therefore stand less of a chance when coping with changes in its environment. Happily, the reverse seems to

(Opposite) Although this Scottish Wildcat looks much like a domestic tabby, the European sub-species does not play any significant part in the ancestry of the domestic cat.

be happening at the moment. Cheetahs are more readily tolerated by farmers than lions or leopards, because they rarely prey on livestock. Correspondingly, their numbers have increased in some parts of Kenya where the other two species have disappeared.

The magnificent big cats have captured the popular imagination, appearing in countless wildlife films, and helping advertizers to sell products ranging from chocolate and sportswear to petrol. Their smaller relatives have remained comparatively unknown, even though there are about thirty-five species and over a hundred tribes. There are basically three branches of the small cats. One diverged about ten million years ago and is now found only in South and Central America. The ocelot is the only representative of this group that is even remotely familiar to most of us, both because it is occasionally kept as an exotic pet, and also because until recently its coat was valued for fur coats. The other members of the ocelot group, the margay, the tiger cat, Geoffroy's cat, the kodkod, the pampas cat and the mountain cat, are scarcely better known to biologists than they are to the general public. They are joined in South America not just by the jaguar, mentioned above, but also by two other descendants of the cats that invaded from Asia across the Bering land bridge. These are the puma and the jaguarundi, both of which still occur in parts of North America. The jaguarundi must rank as having the oddest appearance of any cat; it looks more like a weasel or an otter, and its coat is single-coloured, not blotched, striped or spotted.

The group of cats from which the domestic cat arose first appeared about eight million years ago. Between then and now, many species have probably evolved and gone extinct, without leaving any trace of their existence. The modern species are not easy to classify, but there are four that have no close connection with the domestic cat. These are the jungle cat, which is found from India to Egypt and belies its name by living in all kinds of habitats from swamps to grasslands; and three desert cats, the sand cat in the Sahara desert and Arabia, Pallas' Cat in the cold deserts of Asia, and the Black-footed Cat in southern Africa. All are little-known.

The ancestry of the domestic cat is complicated by the fact that it will interbreed with a group of cats that are found in an

area that stretches from the north of Scotland, to the Cape of Good Hope in South Africa and the steppes of Western China, and very many places in between. Collectively, they are known simply as wildcats. Some biologists divide them into four species: European, African, Indian and Chinese. Because intermediate forms occur wherever these species overlap, it is probably easier to consider them all as wildcats, with the Latin name *Felis sylvestris*.

THE WILDCATS

Wildcats once hunted in the New Forest in Hampshire, a few kilometres from where I live, but today the only British population is in Scotland. A similar race hangs on in those parts of Europe where there are still large tracts of forest. These cats are heavily-built dark-striped tabbies, extremely wary of man, and highly territorial. To the east of Turkey, down into India, and round the north of the Himalayas into China, the various Asian wildcats contrast strikingly with one another. Those living on the cold steppes are long-haired and dark-coated. The Indian Desert Cat is a greyish sandy colour, short-coated and lithe, while the Chinese Desert Cat is pale yellow-grey, and has cm-long ear tufts and hairy feet.

In Africa most of the races are characterized by having reddish fur on the backs of their ears. They also have longer legs than domestic cats, and their walk is loose-limbed, more like that of a cheetah than a cat. Because of these long legs, they sit very upright, like the cats depicted on Egyptian mummy-cases. The length of the coat is not as variable as it is in Asia, and the colour is generally associated with the kind of environment in which the cat lives: the nearer to the desert, the paler the coat and the weaker the stripes. Wildcats are not found in tropical forests, or in the most inhospitable areas of the Sahara and Kalahari deserts, but they seem to be able to live wherever else they can find enough prey to sustain them.

Very few behavioural observations have been made of African or Indian wildcats. They are almost exclusively nocturnal and territorial, and are therefore much less conspicuous than the big cats. They tend to nest underground, but because their paws are not suited to digging this usually means occupying a hole dug by some other species, such as a fox or an ant-bear. Indian wildcats have been recorded as living in haystacks on farms; if these were not hybrids with domestic cats this implies some tolerance of man. Like feral domestic cats, the females bring half-dead prey home to their young kittens, so as to teach them the rudiments of hunting. In one study in India, kittens were killed both by strange male cats and by stray dogs, which probably explains the extreme aggressiveness of the females when they have litters.

The only record of co-operation between wildcats in raising kittens is between a male and a female from different parts of Africa, which mated in captivity in Germany and together raised several litters of kittens. The male was present in the cage when the litters were born, and he would occasionally groom them. However, this may have been due to some effect of captivity. Midwifery and communal nursing, readily seen in domestic cats (*see chapter 7*), have never been observed in wildcats.

Some of the tribes of the wildcat *Felis sylvestris*, with their approximate distribution are shown as shaded areas on the map (*next page*). The European wildcat is a woodland race, which has not adapted to the clearing of the European forests for agriculture and therefore now occurs in small isolated populations. The Near and Middle-Eastern populations, including Tristram's Cat, are quite variable and in places may contain a high proportion of hybrids with the domestic cat. These are bush-cats, living in remote areas but not confined to forests. Tristram's Cat merges, through the population in Iraq and Iran, with the Indian Desert Cat *Felis s. ornata*, which typically inhabits areas of thorny scrub rather than true desert. Moving northwards from the Middle East into Central Asia, various populations of little-studied steppe cats inhabit the dry, cold inhospitable areas north of the Himalayas. From the edge of the Gobi desert in Inner Mongolia, southwards along the eastern edge of the Himalayas to Szechwan in China, lives the Chinese Desert Cat. This may be a separate species, *Felis s. bieti*. Like the Sand Cat, it has hair-covered pads on the souls of its feet, for walking on shifting sands.

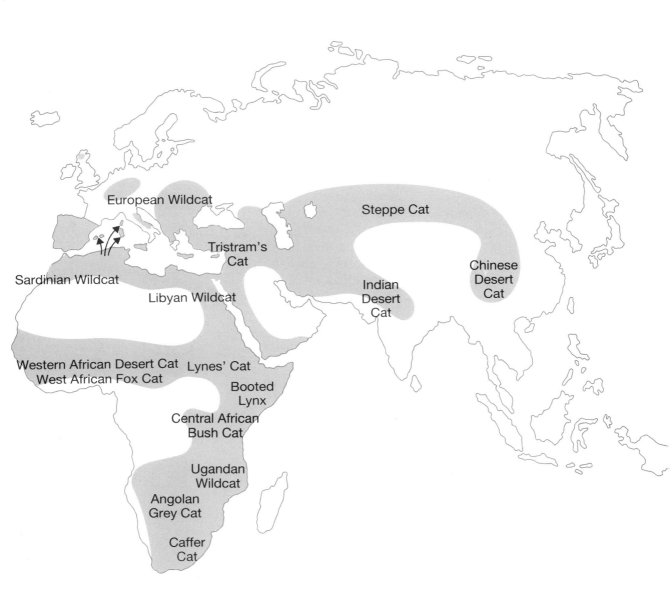

The wildcats of Africa were divided into scores of different subspecies by the mainly British collectors who sent specimens back to the British Museum from every corner of that continent. Collectively these cats are known as *Felis s. lybica*, or African wildcats. Most can be distinguished from European and Indian races, and domestic cats, by the reddish fur covering the backs of their ears. Those in the north-west (Morocco, Tunisia and Algeria) are bush-cats, mainly living on the lower slopes of the Atlas mountains. One of their names, the Sardinian Wildcat, refers to the similarity between these North African cats and the wildcats found on Sardinia, Corsica and Majorca. These islands were probably originally devoid of cats, and those there now are probably the descendants of introductions by man from North Africa. The Libyan Wildcat is more of a desert-dweller than the Sardinian Wildcat, and is distributed across north-east Africa and into the Sinai, where it probably intergrades with the Asian races. Further south on the edge of the Sahara desert in the Sudan and Chad lives the creamy-white Lynes' Cat, named after its discoverer, Rear-Admiral Hubert Lynes. Further west this is replaced by the greyer West African Desert Cat. In the savannahs of West Africa this in turn grades into the West African Fox Cat, named for its striking all-over reddish fur. In Ethiopia lives the Booted Lynx, despite its name a wildcat and not a relative of the true lynx. This is a bush-cat, not a desert cat. A bewildering variety of forms occupy a range of habitats in East Africa, including the cinnamon-coloured Central African Bush Cat, and the strongly-striped Ugandan Wildcat. The Caffer Cat, occupying the Cape, Natal and the Transvaal, is remarkably similar to the Sardinian Wildcat in appearance. North of the Orange River this grades into the Angolan Grey Cat.

THE DOMESTICATION OF THE CAT

It is almost certain that the wildcat was first domesticated in Egypt. In the ancient village of Dier el Medina, near Luxor, tombs dating from 1600 BC contain pictures of domestic scenes that include cats sitting beneath their owners' chairs. Although these cats are striped tabbies just like the local wildcats, the way they are depicted implies that by this time they were already fully domesticated. Bones of cats do turn up in archaeological digs at sites much older than this, but it is usually impossible to tell whether they belong to a pet, or to a wildcat that had been killed for its pelt or for food. Recently, evidence for much earlier domestication was found in Cyprus – a cat's jaw-bone about eight thousand years old. There have probably never been wildcats on Cyprus, so this may have come from a semi-domesticated animal, taken there from Egypt.

The same importation has been suggested for the African-type wildcats that live today on other Mediterranean islands, such as Sardinia, Corsica and Majorca (*see map on page 18*). Some idea of the use they may have been put to comes from a description by the explorer George Schweinfurth of the wildcats of the southern Sudan.

> One of the commonest animals hereabouts was the wildcat of the steppes. Although the natives do not breed them as domestic animals, yet they catch them separately when they are quite young and find no difficulties in reconciling them to a life about their huts and enclosures, where they grow up and wage their natural warfare against the rats. I procured several of these cats, which, after they had been kept tied up for several days, seemed to lose a considerable measure of their ferocity and to adapt themselves to an indoor existence so as to approach in many ways the habits of the common cat. By night I attached them to my parcels, which were otherwise in jeopardy, and by this means I could go together without further fear of any depredation from the rats.

By the time the domestic cat had made its first appearance in the Egyptian paintings, it had already become an important religious object. Male cats were sacred to the sun god Ra, and females to the fertility goddess Basht. Large numbers were kept enclosed within the temples, preventing cross-breeding with local wildcats and thereby accelerating the process of domestication. Presumably for some reason connected with religion, kittens between one and four months old were strangled and mummified, and sent to a huge cat cemetery at Bubastis. These remains lasted until the late nineteenth century, when they were excavated in bulk and sold as fertilizer. From about 1600 BC onwards, cats were also kept as domestic pets, and became highly valued by the whole community. For example, it was made illegal to kill a cat, and when a family pet died, all the members of the household would shave off their eyebrows as a mark of respect. Foreigners were not thought fit to keep cats, and if any did manage to stray abroad they were captured and brought back to Egypt. The pinnacle of reverence towards the cat began in 950 BC, when Basht, the cat goddess, became the national deity. The Romans banned her worship in AD 390.

There must have been an earlier stage of domestication prior to the adoption of the cat as a religious symbol. A likely explanation is that cats were used to control rodent pests in the grain stores that were essential to Egyptian civilization. They may have simply altered their foraging habits to suit this new source of food, and after several thousand generations of living near settlements became sufficiently tolerant of men to be domesticated by the priests. Alternatively, domestication may have started earlier, during the pest-control phase.

Once cats were allowed out of Egypt, they were spread rapidly through Europe by the Romans. Initially, most would have been kept as controllers of vermin, replacing the much less tractable ferrets and polecats that had previously been used for the same purpose. There were domestic cats in India by about 200 BC, and here the Siamese-type breeds began to emerge.

Following centuries of steady expansion, the cat found itself under threat in Europe during the Middle Ages. It became associated with witchcraft and sorcery, and many thousands were killed in the persecution of presumed witches. As recently as the end of the seventeenth century, it was common practice to build the corpse of a cat into the wall of a new building to ward off the Devil. However, cats are among the most adaptable of domestic animals, and weathered this onslaught by adopting a feral lifestyle. In our own century, increasing urbanization has made the cat the preferred pet in many countries, where cats now threaten to, or even actually outnumber dogs. For example, in 1983 the dog population in the USA was about 56 million, and 43 per cent of households owned at least one dog. Between 1983 and 1987, the cat population increased from 52 to 55 million, while the dog population was dropping to 52 million. There is every indication that this trend will continue into the next century, both in America and Europe. The cat seems destined to become not just the most familiar domestic animal for many town-dwellers, but also one of the few animals of any kind with which they will have close contact.

THE ORIGINAL DOMESTIC CAT

There has never been much doubt that the domestic cat is very closely related to the wildcats. Because several of the other small cats can breed successfully with the wildcat, over the years there has been much speculation as to whether the domestic cat is actually some sort of hybrid. The jungle cat used to be a strong candidate, because this species was also kept in Egyptian temples. Paintings dating from 2000 BC, in the tomb of Beni Hassan, depict jungle cats, and their mummified remains have been found in other tombs. However, the Egyptians mummified wild animals of all kinds, so none of this proves that the jungle cat was ever domesticated. Nevertheless, they did keep tame specimens of both species, and hybrids could reasonably have occurred. Remains of cats intermediate in size between the large jungle cats and the smaller African wildcat have been found in Egyptian tombs, and it has been speculated that these were ancestral domestic cats. This is unlikely, because the domestic cat is smaller than either.

Other small cats are less likely candidates. Pallas' Cat, whose tiny ears are almost lost in its long hair, giving it a comical appearance, can be ruled out because it has a different number of chromosomes to the wild cats. The Sand Cat has been put forward, to account for the long hair of some domestic cats, and so has the Leopard Cat, to account for the Siamese cat's unusual vocalizations. Neither of these are necessary. All of the sounds made by Siamese, Persian and ordinary domestic cats have been recorded from captive African wildcats. The long hair of Persian and other breeds can be traced to a simple mutation, and in any case the hair length of wildcats varies considerably between tribes, depending on the climate in which they live.

The whole argument has been finally settled by modern molecular techniques, which have shown that the domestic cat is genetically very similar to the African wildcat. Not only can other species be ruled out, but so too can the European wildcat, which although genetically similar to the domestic cat is not as close as the African. The remaining question is which tribe of cats within Africa is the most likely ancestor. So far the Caffer Cat and the Sardinian Wildcat have been tested, but not the Libyan Wildcat. This last-named has always been the favourite candidate, not only because it occurs in Egypt, but also because it has the smallest skull of any of the African tribes, almost as small as that of the domestic cat.

The slender Indian Desert Cat has been put forward as the ancestor of the oriental breeds, but there is no evidence for domestication taking place anywhere other than in Egypt. It is possible, however, that the early domestic cats picked up some of the characteristics of the local wildcats, after they were transported to settlements in both Europe and Asia. Local wild toms would have been attracted to the domestic females when they came into season, and because they were from the same species, their offspring would have been fertile. Some of these hybrids would have gone wild. This is known to be the case for hybrids between the domestic cat and the Scottish Wildcat or the West African Fox Cat, and possibly others. On the other hand, friendly hybrids are produced when domestic cats mate with some other wildcats, the Ugandan Wildcat for example. If the Indian Desert Cat has contributed some of its genes to the oriental breeds, this is the most likely route.

COATS OF MANY COLOURS

Most of the coat colours that we see in cats today are controlled by just one or two genes, and are inherited in a predictable fashion. They almost certainly arose by mutations, spontaneous changes in the composition of the genetic material. Such mutations are known to occur in wild species, and may persist in free-living populations where they provide some advantage. For example, the black panther is just a non-coloured version of the leopard; the king cheetah is a "blotched tabby" version of the ordinary cheetah. The jaguarundi has red and dark grey forms that were originally described as separate species until both turned up in the same litter. However, most colour variations usually die out in the wild. Colour provides camouflage, and so must suit the animal's surroundings. The different colours of the tribes of the African wildcat fit the environments that they live in, pale and plain for the desert, stripes or spots and red or grey colours for the bush.

The situation is quite different for domestic animals. New colours are prized for their novelty value by the owners of the cats that carry them. Camouflage is no longer so important when man is providing at least part of the cat's food. So long as they are not associated with any adverse effects, new coat colours will not only persist, but may even become common. Some coat colours have survived even though they cause defects. For example, all-white cats (dominant whites, not albino) have defective inner ears and are frequently deaf, which puts them at a great disadvantage when hunting and when looking after kittens (*see Chapter 5*). However, the white coat is so prized in some parts of the world that this gene survives. The Manx gene, although it does not affect coat colour, is another which would die out without human interference. This gene causes a variable reduction in the length of the spine, with the result that only a proportion of embryos are ever viable. Those that survive to be born have little or no tail, and are therefore presumably less adept at balancing than normal cats.

The various coat colours are not evenly distributed around the world; some are apparently favoured in free-living populations, while others rely for their survival on human preferences, which often differ from place to place. For example, the gene that produces orange or partly orange coats (marmalade, tortoiseshell and torbie) is favoured in parts of Asia and also in Scotland, but not to any great extent in other parts of Europe.

Nowadays human preferences do not have much influence on which coat colours predominate in a particular area. When it was commonplace for unwanted kittens to be drowned soon after birth, one with a particularly favourite coat colour might be spared and go on to breed. Now that neutering of pet cats is commonplace, cats of the most preferred colours are actually less likely to breed than those in semi-wild populations. This has been apparent for at least twenty years in Britain. In 1975 Professor Clark of the Institute of Genetics in Glasgow reported that the suburban residents of that city preferred cats with orange or partly white coats and tended to keep cats of those colours, while the cats in run-down areas were usually black or tabby. The number of white or orange cats was not on the increase, however, because they were more likely to have been neutered than blacks or tabbies.

The same preference for orange in the coat was found in the London area in the 1960s. Recently, however, a consistent preference for black cats emerged in a survey carried out by a student of my own, Helen Jones, in Bristol and Southampton. Despite the fact that some of them actually owned marmalade or tortoiseshell cats, many of the cat owners questioned described orange cats as shifty, unpredictable and unfriendly, among other derogatory remarks. If this shift of opinion is genuine, it presumably has some sort of origin in popular culture. Perhaps it is no coincidence that one of the best-known fictional orange cats is the self-centred Garfield.

If there really is any relationship between the colour of a cat's coat and its personality, biologists have yet to investigate it. In some undomesticated carnivores, foxes for example, pale-coated individuals tend to be tamer than dark-coated ones. A hint of a similar relationship in cats has appeared in an unlikely source – a survey of cats killed on roads in Bavaria. Dr Josef Reichholf found that black and black-and-white cats roamed further from their homes than cats of other colours, increasing the chance that they would be run over. The area surveyed was far too large for these cats to be the progeny of one hyperactive black tom, so there may be some genuine connection between the size of a cat's home range (*see Chapter 7*) and its coat.

NINE LIVES?

Cats are undoubtedly the most adaptable of all the domesticated animals. Popular myth states that cats have nine lives, but biologically they have roughly five lifestyles, or niches. These vary from cats which obtain all their food by hunting, and have little or no contact with man, through to the apartment-dweller that may rarely even breathe fresh air. The cat has a flexible relationship with man, and a very flexible demand for space. Once a cat has tasted freedom, it is unlikely that it will take easily to living in a confined space, yet cats brought up in apartments usually seem content to remain there. A cat's primary needs seem to be a reliable source of food and a warm, dry, secure resting-place. Feral cats in the country are probably limited in numbers by how much food is available, unless they become a nuisance and are controlled. In cities, garbage and the food put out by cat-lovers may together provide more edibles than necessary. Instead, the limiting factor seems to be the number of secure resting-sites,

COAT COLOURS

It may come as a surprise to readers that the commonest coat pattern in Britain, the blotched tabby, is not only not found on any of the wildcats, but is also uncommon in many parts of the world. It originated in Britain over 400 years ago, and has been gradually displacing the wildcat striped (mackerel) tabby pattern ever since. Today as many as eight out of ten tabbies in the south of England are blotched, but no one is sure why this pattern has an advantage in Britain. When the British set up colonies overseas, they took their cats with them, and in the new towns and cities that grew up, the proportion of blotched to striped patterns stayed roughly the same. Blotched tabbies are still only about one-third as common as striped tabbies in the eastern United States, where cats arrived about 1650. In Australia, colonized 200 years later, the two patterns are equally common.

The gene that produces the orange coat is both inherited and expressed in a complex way. This is because males have one copy and females have two. Therefore males are either orange or not. Females can be all-orange if they have two copies of the orange gene. If they have only one, it only affects patches of the coat, while the other areas remain the normal brown or black colour. These mixtures are called torbie and tortoiseshell (or calico) respectively. This is an unusual way for genes to be expressed; normally one is dominant over the other so that a cat with one copy looks just the same as a cat with two. For example, the striped tabby is dominant over the blotched; a cat that is genetically mixed striped and blotched will have a striped coat, but can produce blotched kittens.

Black cats are slightly commoner in Britain and north-west Africa than in continental Europe, and are slightly less common in the country than in towns. However, the variations are not great, and black and black-and-white cats make up about a third of most populations. This suggests that cats with one black gene and one normal (which lets the tabby pattern show) are at some sort of advantage over cats with two black genes or two normal. Because the black gene is not dominant, these cats with one copy of each type are not themselves black; their colour is determined by their other genes, so most of them are tabbies. Presumably the gene for black has more effect on a cat's body than simply altering its coat colour, and one of these effects alters survival or breeding success. The genuinely black cat (two copies of the black gene) has some additional advantage of its own in cities, but not in the countryside.

which are particularly important to nesting queens. If their needs for food and resting-places are met, and sexual activity is prevented by neutering, most cats will accept other constraints, such as restricted space.

THE PURE BREEDS

Those readers who are particular fans of one of the "pure"

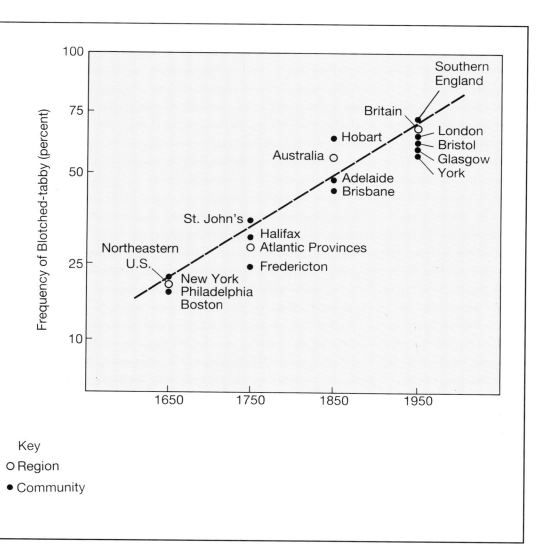

breeds, such as Siamese, Burmese or Persian, will find a great deal of information in this book that applies to their favourite breed. However, biologists have concentrated almost exclusively on the common or garden "moggie" (variously referred to as cross-bred, alley or mongrel cats) derived from European stock. The ancient specialized breeds, all of which originated in Asia, have never been studied systematically, so there is little material on long-haired breeds like the Persian and Angora, nor

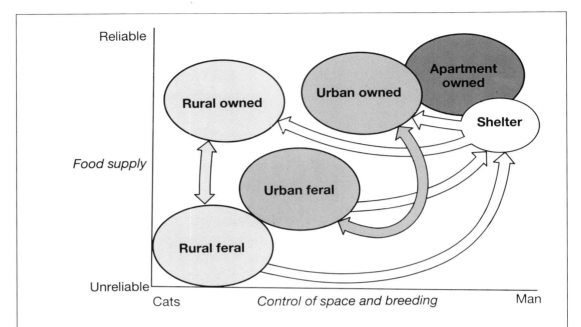

FIVE LIVES

Wherever they live, cats have to make sure that they can balance the amount of control that humans have over them with the amount of food that they provide. The cats that are at least dependent on humans live in the countryside ("rural feral"). They hunt for much of their food, and may starve if prey is scarce or if there is too much competition from other predators (including cats). On the other hand, they are rarely neutered, and can therefore select a mate and produce young just as if they were wild animals. Some degree of dependence on man ("rural owned") brings with it the advantage of a more reliable food supply than hunting can provide, something that is particularly useful in winter or for a female with dependent kittens. The probability of being neutered is,

however, higher than for the rural feral.

In towns, free-ranging cats ("urban feral") are controlled both directly and indirectly by people. Where the cats become a nuisance, they may be poisoned or trapped. Those caught by animal welfare organizations will be neutered or euthanized. The best urban habitats are often derelict areas, which may disappear as they are redeveloped. Ownership ("urban owned") has both advantages and disadvantages. The probability of being neutered increases, often to above 80 per cent. On the other hand, a house with a garden provides a ready-made territory which the owner may help to defend against other cats. The most confined cats live in apartments without access to the outdoors; these cats have a

guaranteed lifestyle, but will almost certainly never be able to breed.

Transfers between these lifestyles can occur spontaneously, or through human intervention, as indicated by the arrows. In both town and country, feral cats can "adopt" one or more households to obtain regular food; they, or their kittens, may subsequently become pets.

If an owned cat's supply of food disappears, possibly if it has been abandoned, it may temporarily "go wild" in an attempt to survive. Animal rescuers ("shelter") provide another route from feral to owned status; some ferals may be too unsociable to become pets, but their offspring can be trained if handled from an early age, before being homed.

the slender-bodied Oriental breeds like the Siamese and Burmese. The one exception is that vision has been studied in Siamese cats, some strains of which are prone to squints (*see Chapter 2*). What little information there is about specialized breeds has been documented in the USA, and may be less applicable to Europe. Everyone seems to agree that, in any case, cats vary as much from individual to individual as they do between breeds. Cat personalities are discussed in Chapter 8.

Persian cats are generally less active than other breeds, and tend not to be lap cats. Perhaps the combined effect of the warmth of their owner and their long hair makes prolonged contact with people an uncomfortably warm experience. On the other hand, it could be due to a difference in temperament, because the short-haired Abyssinians are also disinclined to sit on laps.

More reliable differences are apparent when comparing Siamese and Burmese cats with other breeds. These oriental cats are noisy, active and highly responsive to everything that goes on around them. They are also reputed to be easier to train than moggies. Many are very affectionate and crave bodily contact with their owners, although this may be because of a simple desire for warmth brought on by their thin coats. Burmese cats generally display the same characteristics as Siamese, but to a lesser degree. Some strains of Burmese tend to aggression, prompting leading cat behaviour counsellor Dr Peter Neville to describe them jokingly as "the Rotweillers of the cat world".

COAT AND SKIN

Cats have surprisingly loose skin, which probably contributes to their legendary suppleness. The skin is also useful protection in fights, increasing the probability that a bite will only produce a superficial wound. Most cats are double-coated, that is their coat consists of long, strong guard hairs on top, which produce the colour and pattern of the coat, and beneath these a second layer of shorter, softer hairs that provide insulation. Selective breeding has produced modifications to one or both of these layers. Angora cats have extra-long guard hairs and shorter hairs underneath, while Persians have both types long. Cornish Rex have no guard hairs.

WALK, TROT, GALLOP.

Cats have three types of gait. A walking cat moves its legs in the following order; right hindleg, right foreleg, left hindleg, left foreleg and so on. Each foot is placed almost precisely in front of the last, so that the pawprints of a walking cat are nearly all in a straight line. If the cat wants to move a little faster, it will break into a trot. This is similar to the walk, except that the diagonally opposite legs move almost simultaneously. The gallop, on the other hand, is quite different. The domestic cat never seems to use the full bound gallop, in which both front legs are touched down together, then both hind legs.

Most cats can perform three different gallops, although most individuals have a preference for one or the other. They are: transverse gallop (right foreleg, left foreleg, ▶

The coat can be fluffed out at will, either to increase insulation in cold weather, or to make the cat look larger when it is confronting a rival. In the latter situation, the tail hairs stand straight out, producing the well-known "bottle-brush" effect.

If you had to wear a fur coat all the time, you would overheat very quickly. Cats run their metabolism at a lower rate than ours, and so do not generate so much internal heat. This is just as well, because they can only sweat from the soles of their feet, resulting in damp footprints in hot weather. They can pant like a dog, although they tend to avoid having do to this by not charging about as dogs do. If cats get really hot, they smear their coats with saliva, which provides some cooling as it evaporates.

Most of the time, cats groom themselves with a dry tongue, combing rather than washing. The "comb" consists of a large patch of backward-pointing hooks on the top surface of the tongue. As well as being used for tasting, the cat's tongue can also be turned into a spoon for lapping liquids. Four or five "spoonfuls" are flicked up into the mouth between each swallow.

UNDER THE SKIN

Beneath their soft exteriors, cats are hardly modified from the wild hunters that still stalk the African plains and deserts. Domestication has scarcely blunted their potential to find and kill prey, although the extent to which each cat exercises those powers depends on its early experiences, as described in Chapter 4. Cats are mammals, and have a skeleton, teeth and

muscles that are based on a pattern not very different from our own, but modified in many ways to suit the lifestyle of their ancestors.

Have you ever wondered how a cat manages to be so lithe? Running from each of your shoulders to your throat is a prominent bone, the clavicle or collar-bone, which keeps your shoulders a fixed distance apart. In the cat, this bone is reduced to a fragment and replaced by strong muscles. This enables the shoulders to move very freely, which in turn helps the cat both to walk along the top of a fence, and to twist its front limbs in mid-pounce. More flexibility comes from the long back, equipped with unusually loose-jointed vertebrae. The hind legs are built more for power than flexibility. They provide most of the motive force for walking and running, and all of the power of the pounce.

Like most of the members of the cat family, the domestic cat walks on its toes and not on its heels. Compared to human feet, the cat's foot-bones are greatly elongated, an adaptation to fast running on all fours. That is why the joint nearest the end of the cat's leg bends forwards, not backwards; this joint is the cat's ankle, whereas its knee is much higher up, on its flank. Cats are sprinters, not long-distance runners, but they are nowhere near as fast as their relative, the cheetah, which is built exclusively for speed.

Skulls are able to provide a biologist with many clues to an unknown animal's way of life. Even fossil skulls can provide a great deal of information, not just suggested lifestyles, but even clues as to how intelligent extinct animals may have been. The

▼ right hindleg, left hindleg), the rotatory gallop (right foreleg, left foreleg, left hindleg, right hindleg), and the half-bound (right foreleg, left foreleg, both hindlegs together). After the last hind leg has left the ground, there is a period of flight in which no foot is touching the ground. If a cat has to gallop any distance, it can switch smoothly from one type of gallop to another, and can also change which foot leads.

It has been found that the front legs produce no overall propulsion when the cat is walking, and do little more than support the relatively heavy head and shoulders. As the cat puts its front feet down on the ground, they actually slow it up slightly, and by the time they are lifted again, they have only provided just enough forward motion to cancel out this braking effect. If the front legs were doing most of the work, this would produce a very jerky walk, but of course the cat's walk is actually very smooth, almost fluid. Cleverly, the braking effect of the front legs is counteracted by the hind legs, which are pushing forwards powerfully at precisely the same moment.

cat's skull has huge eye-sockets, showing that it was derived from a nocturnal hunter, and jaws and teeth that are specialized for eating meat. There are only thirty adult teeth, a smaller number than most carnivores have, although some cats, including the lynx, have two fewer. If you can persuade your cat to open its mouth for long enough for you to have a look, it will be obvious that the front teeth, the incisors, would never be able to bite into an apple the way we do with ours. They are tiny teeth, six top and six bottom, used mainly for grooming. Next to them are the four canines, the killer teeth. These are long, slightly flattened and, unlike our own, very sensitive to pressure, particularly from the side. Thus cats can probe the backbone of a rat with their canines, judging the precise point where a sudden bite will cause these teeth to slip between and dislocate two vertebrae.

Behind the canine teeth are premolars and molars, the largest of which are known as carnassials, specialized slicing teeth that slide past one another like the blades of a pair of shears to cut meat into chewable fragments. Cats do not have flat-topped molars like ours, so that they slice, rather than crush or grind, their food when they chew.

The other main adaptation to hunting is the claws. Equivalent to our finger- and toe-nails, they are made from keratin, a protein, but each nail is anchored to a toe-bone, providing rigidity. Like human nails, they grow continuously, and the points have to be sharpened by stropping them on a tree-trunk or specially-provided scratching-post. Normally, the claws are hidden under a fold of skin at the front of each pad. When they are needed, muscles in the toes rotate the end toe-bones forwards, which automatically push out the claws. Like the canine teeth, the claws are not only sharp, they are also equipped with sense organs that tell the cat just how much resistance they are meeting.

Thus the cat's head and feet immediately betray its origins as a wild predator. As we will see in the next chapter, its senses are also tuned to the lifestyle of a hunter.

CHAPTER 2

The World Your Cat Lives In

Some animals lead such unusual lives that we naturally expect them to have a different view of the world to our own. Bats provide one of the best-known examples; the ultrasonic detection system by which they guide their headlong flights is so foreign to our own experience that we tend to compare it to a mechanical device – radar – rather than to our own ability to navigate by reflected sounds (although blind people can and do learn to use this method of gauging their surroundings). It seems natural that an animal that lives in the sea, even a mammal like a dolphin or a whale, should have its senses tuned differently to our own. Because the cat shares our homes and lives alongside us day by day, it is easy to assume that it can hear, see, feel, smell and taste everything that we can, and vice versa. However, we now know that in each and every one of those senses, the cat has different abilities to ours; many superior, some inferior. To be certain, there is a great deal of overlap, since we are both mammals, and also get around by walking, rather than flying or swimming. The reasons why the domestic cat is different can be traced back to the evolution of the small cats as specialized hunters, whose very survival depended on their ability to find, stalk, pounce and kill. Most of the cat's special abilities can be explained in this way; domestication seems to have had little effect on the kind of information that the cat gathers in from its surroundings, although it may have changed the way that it reacts to that information.

BALANCE AND TOUCH

Most people admit that their cat has a superior sense of balance to their own, acrobats excepted! The cat has four feet, giving it an unfair advantage over our two, but this cannot explain the whole of the difference; when were you last greeted by a dog walking confidently along the top of a fence? The powerhouse of the sense of balance is the vestibular system, which provides the cat with detailed information on its orientation in space, and its direction and rate of change of movement (*see illustration on page 38.*). This organ is found in all mammals, including humans, but that of the cat has a few special features. The three semi-circular canals are arranged almost precisely at right angles, which should produce clearer information than our own, which are imperfectly aligned. Moreover, in the cat the horizontal canal is precisely parallel to the angle at which the head is normally held, and small deviations from this angle are precisely those to which the gravity-detecting system is most sensitive. However, these refinements cannot on their own account for the cat's acrobatic abilities. So it is reasonable to assume that it is the use to which the information is put, as much as the quality of that information, which gives the cat the inborn ability to balance in situations which would require endless practice by a person.

The balance organ is "wired" through its nerves to the brain, so that the cat can actually "know" and feel where it is in space. However, the brain takes time to process information and then act on it, and if this was the only route from the balance organ to the cat's muscles, the whole system would probably be too slow to work effectively. Much more quick-acting are the many nervous connections that run directly from the balance organ to the most important muscles, bypassing the brain completely. These are reflexes, like the one that causes your lower leg to jerk when you are tapped just below the kneecap. The simplest to understand are those that connect the balance organ to the eyes. If you turn your head slightly to one side, you will find that it is natural to keep your gaze fixed on the same spot. If you think about it, this means that your eye must have swivelled in exactly the opposite direction to compensate for the motion of your head (the same thing actually happens in the dark, so it is the balance organ and not the eye itself that triggers the movement). If you turn your head right round to the side, further than your eye can swivel, it will make several jerky movements to compensate, fixing momentarily on a new object each time. If it were possible to move your head without turning your eyes at all, your vision would be blurred, but the reflexes are so strong that this is almost impossible to do, unless you raise your hand in front of your face and swivel that too.

There are quite a number of these reflexes in the cat, that allow it to fix its gaze, say on potential prey, while moving its head and body in a highly controlled way. If a cat sees something moving from the corner of its eye, it will first fix its gaze by moving its eye in that direction, and will then turn its head to face it, while gradually moving its eyes to maintain the gaze. Other reflexes connecting the balance organ and the eyes compensate for other types of movement, such as the jolts and jars received by the head when the cat is moving at a gallop or over rough ground.

These reflexes are essential to the hunting cat; once it has its prey in view, it can ill afford to lose sight of it again. As will be explained in the next chapter, out-of-sight is almost as good as out-of-mind to cats, which have only a limited ability to work out where things that disappear have gone.

If you watch a cat stalking, you can hardly fail to be impressed by the way in which it can keep its head steady while the rest of its body is moving; the same ability can be seen in other predators that rely on vision, such as birds of prey. This steadiness is largely achieved by the neck muscles, which are triggered into action by another set of reflexes originating in the balance organ. As soon as a movement of the head is detected, the corresponding muscle in the neck is activated, restoring the head to its original position even though the angle of the body has now changed. Still more reflexes link the balance organ with muscles in the body, and there are even positional detectors in the neck that modify the way that these reflexes act.

However, robot-like speed and precision are needed when

a cat suddenly loses its footing and falls, if it is to avoid serious injury. The feet and shoulders of cats are marvellous shock-absorbers, so if the falling cat is upright, the first thing it needs to do is to prepare its legs for landing. Within seven-hundredths of a second, the otoliths in the balance organs have detected the sudden acceleration caused by the fall, and reflexes have begun to extend the legs. A more awkward fall will require the cat to twist in mid-air, and this is accomplished as a two-stage process; first the head is twisted into its normal position, then it is followed by the body.

Of course, the balance organ is not the only way that a cat can tell which way up it is; vision plays an important part as well. Part of a cat's skill in balancing is due to its very sensitive feet (a benefit of going barefoot!), and positional information can come from almost anywhere on the skin as the cat brushes against objects along its way. The skin of the cat is equipped with a battery of touch, heat and pain receptors similar to our own, and although the detailed construction, and density, of each is not identical to ours, it is difficult to say whether cats have a similar sense of touch to us or not (even allowing for the difference in hairiness). The hairy skin does indeed contain a large number of specialist receptors that respond to stroking, which may or may not be part of the reason why cats like being stroked. Other receptors respond to brief touch, more sustained touch, stretching of the skin, and so on.

The cat's sense of touch is mostly concentrated on its feet and nose, and at the bases of the sensory hairs. These are much stiffer and thicker than normal hairs; the most obvious are, of course, the whiskers, known scientifically as the mystacial vibrissae. There are other, shorter vibrissae on the head; a superciliary tuft above each eye, and two genal tufts on each side of the head. Most carnivores, including the dog, have another tuft of vibrissae under their lower jaws; none of the cat family have these, perhaps because they are only useful to animals that hunt by following scents, with their noses close to the ground

Where the vibrissae are bedded in the skin there are very large numbers of touch receptors, sending information on the amount, direction and speed of any bending of a vibrissa. The whiskers themselves can be moved backwards for protection when the cat is defending itself, and forwards, to help to position

As soon as a cat realises it is falling, it twists its head round so that it can see where it is going to land. It tucks its paws into its chest to speed up the turn, just as a skater spins faster when she holds her arms at her sides. Once the head is pointing downwards, the back half of the body can follow. Only then are the legs extended and the back arched, ready for the landing.

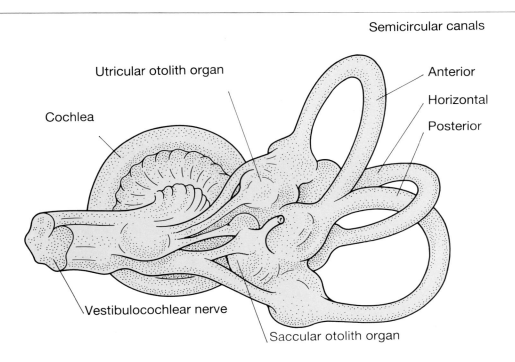

Semicircular canals

Utricular otolith organ

Anterior

Horizontal

Posterior

Cochlea

Vestibulocochlear nerve

Saccular otolith organ

THE VESTIBULAR SYSTEM

The vestibular system is the key to the cat's exquisite sense of balance, but in form it is similar to the same organ found in man and other mammals. It is found in the inner ear, well protected by the bones of the skull and close to the brain where the information it produces is analyzed. The three semi-circular canals radiate out from its centre, each one roughly at right angles to the other two. They are filled with fluid and lined with sensitive hairs that detect movements of the fluid. What happens when the cat turns its head is the fluid stays where it was, and the walls of the canal twist around.

You can demonstrate this effect for yourself with a dish of water with something small floating on the surface; turn the dish smoothly a quarter of a turn to the left, and the floating object (and the water) will remain where it was. This mimics the horizontal canal, which responds when the cat turns its head to left or right. Of the other two canals, one is primarily responsible for sensing when the cat looks up or down, and the other for when it puts its head on one side. Incidentally, if you continue to rotate the dish, the water will eventually begin to turn as well, and once started will continue even after the dish has stopped; this is the reason why children can make

themselves feel giddy by spinning round and round and then stopping.

The other two parts of the vestibular organ work on a slightly different principle. These are the utricular and saccular otolith organs, which detect acceleration and deceleration (speeding up or slowing down in any direction) and gravity, so a cat can always know which way is "up". The otoliths are tiny crystals of calcite, hundreds of which cover the sensory surface of these organs. Because of their high density they get momentarily left behind as the cat's head moves, brushing against minute hairs that send impulses to the nervous system.

the snout most effectively when an object is being sniffed or bitten. Much smaller sensory hairs found along the outer edges of the lips probably help with the latter function. The importance of the whiskers, and the hairless skin of the nose, can be judged from the large area of brain that is devoted to interpreting touch information from the front part of the face.

The other specialized areas of touch are on the forepaws, which are used in play, for exploring the surfaces of unfamiliar objects and manipulating food. On the wrists, specialized carpal hairs provide information about the terrain and the cat's movement over it. The skin of the pads (affectionately known as "baked beans" in white-socked cats) is packed with touch receptors. When these are stroked, they may conceivably produce a sensation like being tickled, accounting for the reluctance of some cats to be touched on underside of their feet. Each pad is very sensitive to the direction and speed of movement with

(Below) A distorted view of the cat shows the importance of each area of the skin in the sense of touch. The face is most over-emphasized, followed by the forepaws. In animals that hunt largely by touch, such as raccoons, the forepaws account for even more of the touch-processing capacity of the brain.

which something brushes across its surface, but they are not particularly good for discriminating between textures if the pad is placed directly on a surface. This is probably why cats explore novel objects by stroking and patting them. Furthermore, the pads are not the only sensitive part of the feet. Once they have been extended, the claws also become sense organs, each equipped with a set of positional detectors that inform the cat of the pressure and twist that each is receiving, invaluable information to a cat that is manipulating prey or climbing.

HEARING

Given the very sensitive pads on their soles, not to mention the carpal hairs, cats can probably "hear" a great deal through their feet, but airborne sounds are detected mainly in their ears. We will examine the workings of these from the outside inwards , so to speak, to show just how exquisitely adapted the cat's hearing is.

The part of the ear that we can see is known technically as the pinna (somehow "ear lobe" does not sound right when referring to a cat), and the construction of this is absolutely critical in determining how much use cats can make of the sounds that reach them. The pinna is funnel-shaped, like a megaphone in reverse, and gathers sounds from the air, amplifying them as they pass towards the middle ear. The greatest boost is provided for sounds that are quite high-pitched to us, at frequencies of 2,000-6,000 hertz. It has been suggested that this ensures the best possible detection of the calls of kittens and other cats, but no one has put this directly to the test. Certainly, the human ear is tuned to the frequencies of human speech, but then we are much more vocal than most cats.

A hunting cat pays great attention to sounds as important indicators of the location of potential prey, and successful hunting means pinpointing exactly from where those sounds are coming. Cats that are deaf in one ear are poor locators of sounds, and often make exaggerated movements of their heads in their attempts to pin a noise down to its source. Two ears are therefore much better than one for this task, and we now know that cats make careful comparisons between the sounds arriving at each ear, and can deduce instantly from which direction they are coming, an ability we also have, but to a lesser extent. However, the way the direction is calculated varies depending on the pitch of the sound. Medium to low-pitched sounds (below about 500 hertz) have long wavelengths, and are difficult to pinpoint, simply because the cat's head is too small for each ear to receive different parts of the wave. Between about 500 and 4,000 hertz, time differences between the sounds are used to indicate their direction. This works as follows: for a sound coming from straight ahead, the peak of each sound wave will hit both ears at exactly the same time. For a sound to the left of the head, by the time a peak reaches the right ear, a trough will be approaching the left ear, and for a sound to the right, the opposite will apply. This method works well until, at about 5,000 hertz, the lengths of the sound waves become so short that confusion sets in as to how many wavelengths delay there is between left and right ears. There might be several if the sound was right out to the side, or only one if it was almost dead ahead; the sound perceived would be exactly the same. So for high-pitched sounds direction is simply judged by which ear hears the more muffled sounds, as the head itself absorbs some of the sound as it passes across it. This last method is only really efficient for sounds that are too high-pitched for humans to hear at all, which means that cats have a "dip" in their direction-finding abilities between medium and ultra-high frequencies. Since natural sounds usually consist of a mix of frequencies, in practice cats can use both methods simultaneously, and presumably compare the answer from one with the answer from the other, because they achieve much more accurate discriminations of direction with complex sounds than with single notes.

So far, we have only been considering sounds that come from in front, or to the sides. The problem of deciding from what height a sound has come needs a quite different solution, since cats have their ears set on either side of their head, not one above the other. Kittens, in particular, often attempt to produce the latter effect by putting their heads on one side, an expression of instant appeal to ourselves because it mimics the human body-language for puzzlement. However, what they may really be doing is improving the accuracy of their sound-locating system. The key to this system is visible just inside the pinna. The complex corrugations there have two functions. One is simply to make the pinna stand up straight; the other is to produce subtle distortions of high-pitched sounds as they arrive at the ear, causing some frequencies to get slightly louder, and others slightly quieter. This boosting is entirely dependent on direction (both up-and-down and side-to-side); working with models of pinnae, scientists have even found that particular notes actually appear louder at the more distant ear. By comparing these subtle distortions, the exact height of the sound can be worked out, but only if it contains a mix of frequencies; cats, like us, cannot judge the height of a single pure note, and it is probably no coincidence that the calls of many small birds consist of precisely that – single pure notes. The ability to recognize the height of a sound must rely on learning, for two reasons. One is that, like our fingerprints, the inside of every cat's pinna is different, and it is highly unlikely that the brain could be programmed in advance with the precise frequency distortions that each cat's unique design will produce. The other is that the pinna grows with the cat, and so its directional properties will change, confusingly, throughout kittenhood; perhaps it is not too far-fetched to think of the kitten's "head-on-one-side" expression as puzzlement over the new sounds it is hearing, as well as a check on their accuracy.

One ability that the cat has, that we clearly do not, is the ability to swivel its pinnae, either together or one at a time. Physics tells us that this should make working out the direction of sounds more difficult, rather than easier, because matching of the sounds from the two ears becomes much more complex. It has been suggested that mobile pinnae spread direction-finding over the full 360 degrees, but how the brain makes allowances for the swivelling in interpreting the sounds is still a mystery.

The detection of the sounds is done in the middle ear and inner ear, buried in the skull and connected to the pinna by the ear canal. The sound waves in the air cause the ear drum to vibrate, and this in turn causes vibrations in tiny bones, called ossicles, which transmit the sound into the fluid-filled cavities of the inner ear. It is here that the analysis of the sound begins, by nerve cells, some individually tuned to particular notes and others to changes in pitch. What is special about the cat's hearing is the enormous range of notes (or frequencies) that can be detected. Generally speaking, the hearing range of a mammal can be predicted from the size of its head; small heads contain small ears, and small ears respond better to high frequencies,

while large ears work better at low frequencies. For example, mice can hardly hear human speech at all, but can hear, and indeed communicate by, high-pitched sounds like the squeaks of bats. Elephants, on the other hand, communicate over huge distances with low-pitched rumbles that just feel like vibrations in the ground to us. Remarkably, the cat has not only its expected hearing range, but also about an octave's extension at either end; this means that it can hear all but the highest-pitched squeaks of small rodents, its typical prey, and also the full range of human speech. The average cat can detect much quieter noises than the average person, and this will be particularly apparent when the sound contains a high-proportion of high-frequency components, like the rustles and scratchings of a foraging mouse.

Our own sense of hearing may not be quite as good as the cat's at picking up very small noises, but in other respects humans have the edge, and this is reflected in the complexity of our speech when compared to the relatively simple sounds that cats make. For example, we are better at discriminating small differences in volume, and better at detecting sounds of very short duration. It is difficult to tell whether cats' perception of the harmonies of music is the same as ours. However, it is as true of hearing as it is of all the other senses that we can only guess at what are the cat's subjective impressions of sounds. People's abilities can be measured by asking them questions about what they hear. Cats have to be laboriously trained to perform some task, such as pressing a lever when they hear a particular sound, and it is quite possible that under such artificial conditions they do not give of their best.

Certainly, the overall impression of the cat's hearing is that it is almost entirely tuned to locating the tiny noises made by prey. One mystery remains; why can cats also hear the relatively low-pitched sounds of male speech, when by rights a mammal of their size should not? Whatever quirk of evolution originally shaped that ability, it is tempting to speculate that it was one of the factors that aided the domestication of the cat.

VISION . . . HOW DO CATS SEE?

As I am writing these words, my cat Lucy is gazing past me out of the window, fascinated by the leaves being blown past in the wind. She is rather small, so her eyes seem even bigger and more appealing than those of other cats. Even human babies do not have such large eyes in proportion to the size of their heads as cats do, and part of the appeal that cats have is their infant-like faces. However, when we consider the way that vision works in the cat, good reasons emerge for their large eyes and their fascination with movement.

In fact, the eye of the average cat is only slightly smaller than our own, but the maximum size of the pupil, the black part of the eye that lets in the light, can expand to over three times the area of ours. This, and many other special features of the cat's eye, combine to produce great visual sensitivity. Neither cats nor people can see in the pitch dark, but cats can see a great deal more than we can when there is only the faintest glimmer of light.

Before we go on to discover the inner workings of the cat's eye, we need to consider how the cat protects its super-sensitive vision on sunny days. Most cats love sunbathing, and they cannot always keep their eyes closed in bright sunlight, but cats' eyes are protected by muscles in the iris, the coloured part of the eye. In bright light, these reduce human pupils to about 2 mm (1/12 in) in diameter, but this would not be enough to protect the cat's delicate retina. As a circular pupil cannot get much smaller than this, the cat's pupil narrows not into a circle but into a slit, which can be closed completely save for a tiny pinhole at each end.

The other unusual feature of a cat's eye which can be observed directly is the eye-shine apparent when the cat is caught in a beam of light after dark. This eye-shine is due to a reflective layer of cells behind the retina, known as the tapetum, which enhance dark vision. Much of the light that enters human eyes falls between the visually-sensitive cells of the retina and is absorbed, undetected, in the back of the eye. Many nocturnal mammals give this wasted light a second chance to be detected, by having a tapetum which reflects it back the way it came. Just as the first pass through the retina was not totally efficient, so some light passes back through the retina and re-emerges through the pupil, creating the eye-shine. Much of the light is trapped, however, and it is estimated that, in the cat, the tapetum increases the efficiency of the eye by about 40 per cent.

The retina is the real powerhouse of the eye, turning the light into nerve impulses which are used by the brain to produce vision. In the human eye, the cones, used for daylight vision, are concentrated in the middle of the retina, the part that gives an image of whatever we are looking at directly. The rods, used for night vision, are packed around the outside of the retina, recording peripheral vision, and there are none at all in the central fovea, which is packed with cones. This is why at night it is often easier to see something if you stare slightly away from it, but during the day the opposite is true. Nowhere on the cat's retina does the density of cones reach more than 20 per cent of that in the human fovea, and the cones are always interspersed with rods. So cats are provided with a much more complete and brighter image after dark, at the expense of poorer vision in daylight. The chances of picking up a faint glimmer of light are further improved by large numbers of rods being connected to each nerve that passes information to the brain, with the result that although the density of rods is up to three times higher in the cat, the number of nerve fibres in the optic nerve is more than ten times higher in human eyes.

(Below) A diagram of the cat's eye. Light enters the pupil from the left, is focussed by the lens, and forms an image on the retina at the right where it is detected by the rods and also (in daylight) by the cones (shown magnified). These send nerve impulses through the optic nerve to the brain where the image is formed. Light that misses the rods and cones is reflected back by the tapetum; as it passes the rods and cones again it has a second chance of being detected, or it may re-emerge through the pupil, producing the cat's "eye-shine".

In contrast to all this detailed structural information, our knowledge of how the eyes adjust from close to distant vision is incomplete, so it would be difficult to design effective spectacles for cats! One of the problems has been that most of the studies have been done on cats that live most of their lives indoors, and whose eyes have become "lazy", never needing to travel from near to distant objects and back. There is certainly a difference between the resting eye state of feral cats, which tend to be long-sighted, and indoor cats, which tend to become short-sighted. However, it is generally agreed that cats focus their

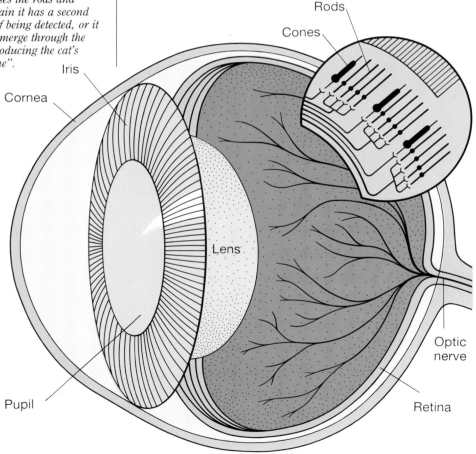

Rods

Cones

Iris

Cornea

Lens

Pupil

Optic nerve

Retina

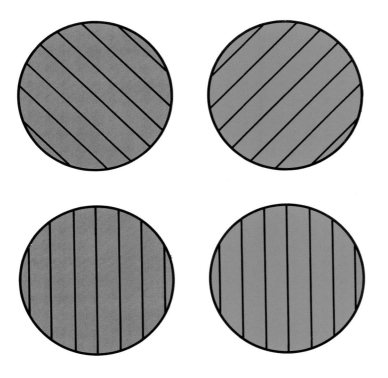

that in daylight its vision is more blurred than ours, and only faintly coloured. Are there any other differences between what we see and what cats see? Because they cannot tell us what things look like to them, this is not an easy question to answer. One way that this subjective world of vision can be investigated is through illusions. These can give the ways in which a human, or an animal, makes sense of the complex pictures that their eyes produce. They work because they "cheat" the brain into misusing its processes for simplification of images, so that we see something that is not really there. One example of a simple, familiar illusion that cats probably also see is shown on the next page.

One process that is essential is the recognition that various visual features belong to the same object; for example its outline, its colours, its surface texture, its depth, and so on. For example, a cat walking down the street sees another cat sitting in a window, partly hidden by one of the window bars. Does the

SEEING IN COLOUR

In the early 1960s, Donald Meyer and Roy Anderson of Ohio State University first trained cats to distinguish between objects with different patterns and colours, and then "weaned them off" the pattern. This was done, cleverly, by drawing diagonal patterns in two colours. Initially, the cats were trained to choose one of a pair of objects like those at the top, with the stripes running in opposite directions. This they did easily, presumably because they are very perceptive of patterns. Then, between each training session, the objects were rotated a little in opposite directions, until both patterns were vertical and therefore identical, like the pair below. The cats transferred their attention from the patterns to the colours, and finally "realized" that the colour was the important cue.

first cat think "there are the front half and the back half of a cat, on opposite sides of that window", or does it think (as we would) "there is a cat sitting in that window". In other words, does it join up the two halves it can see, using imaginary lines that pass across the window bar? Careful training experiments have indicated that cats can indeed do this, and this kind of process is probably essential to a cat that is hunting in cover, otherwise it would have to keep re-identifying prey every time part of it disappeared behind the vegetation.

Movement seems to hold a particular fascination for cats, particularly rapid or jerky movements. In fact they pay remarkably little attention to very slow movements, and appear to be barely capable of noticing motion that is ten times faster than the slowest that we can detect. This may be a situation akin to colour vision, in that they may simply regard slow movements as irrelevant. Their eyes are, however, highly tuned to pick up rapid movements, and this must be particularly important to the hunting cat, which needs to judge the precise direction and speed with which it should make its pounce. At one time it was thought that the cat might possess a counterpart to the hunting specializations in the eye of the frog. Frogs have a "fly-detecting" system that processes visual information; objects that are the size of a fly and move like a fly are detected by dedicated nerves, which help to aim the frog's sticky tongue as it flicks out. The frog does not therefore have to think about where the fly is and how fast and in what direction it is moving. By the time information had been digested by the brain the fly would have moved on, and the frog's tongue would have been launched in the wrong direction. However, although cats do have some impressive and sophisticated movement-processing machinery, its output is more complex, and is used in a more flexible way than the frog's.

Cats are also good at recognizing shapes. Squares are easily distinguished from triangles, and short, squat triangles from tall, thin ones. Even shapes whose edges are defined by changes in texture rather than by solid edges appear just as real to cats as they are to us.

We have already established that cats have binocular vision, but how do they judge how far away things are? It is theoretically possible that they could rely on differences in focus between close objects and distant ones. Humans get some distance information in this way, as you can see for yourself by closing one eye and focussing in turn on one of the top corners of this book, and then on an object slightly to one side but in the other corner of the room. If you do this again with both eyes open, a much more obvious effect appears: when you are looking across the room the book appears to have two corners, which fuse together as your eyes re-focus on the book. This method of judging depth, known as retinal disparity, seems to be the cat's primary method. It must develop gradually, since a kitten's binocular vision, and its judgement of depth, are considerably inferior to that of an adult cat. A great deal of visual experience is required for vision to develop fully, in contrast to the situation in many other mammals, rabbits for example, where visual abilities are pre-programmed and develop spontaneously. The cat's slow development is probably linked to its binocular vision. For this to be accurate, the cat must "know" how far apart its eyes are. Since a kitten's skull will grow at a variable rate depending on, for example, how well fed it is, the precise distance between its eyes not only changes as it grows, but also changes unpredictably. Continuous adjustments therefore have to be made, to ensure that the perception of distance in the adult is perfectly tuned for hunting.

Many Siamese cats unfortunately never develop proper stereoscopic vision, because they lack the nerve cells that compare the input from each eye and make the 3-D images. This is why many Siamese develop squints, like children with poor vision in one eye tend to do. However, most Siamese cats seem to be able to get about and even hunt perfectly well, so this disability does not seem to be much of a drawback for a well-cared-for pet.

THE SENSE OF TASTE

Just as we are unlikely ever to be able to imagine exactly what a cat sees, so it is impossible for us to taste in the same way as a cat does. Of course, there are a great many things that cats like to taste that we might not be able to bring ourselves to try! The cat's taste buds are to be found on its tongue, like our own, and superficially at least look rather similar. However, the cat's

(Opposite) Our own brains are always trying to simplify and "make sense" of the visual information that they see. All of the figures opposite consist of eight white three-quarter circles arranged within a black rectangle. However, when the circles are arranged in certain ways, like those on the left hand side, four of them seem to produce a black square. The square does not actually have any sides, but it is hard to believe that they are not there, and some people "see" faint grey lines filling in the gaps between the "corners" that are defined by the white discs. Other arrangements of the eight circles, like the ones in the column on the right, produce no such illusions. Cats can be trained to distinguish between sequences of these pictures that suggest a moving square (top to bottom, on the left), from those that produce no such illusion (top to bottom, on the right). This seems to prove that they, also, join up the missing parts of an outline to make sense of what is likely to be a single object; these missing parts are known as subjective contours.

distaste for many foods that we find appealing suggests that they do not perceive tastes in the same way that we do. This makes sense, as we will see in Chapter 4, because not only does their natural diet consist almost entirely of meat, but also their bodies have adapted to this diet, to the extent that their nutritional requirements are different to ours in a whole host of important details. In other words, what is good for us is not necessarily good for a cat, and so it is reasonable to assume that what tastes good to us will not always taste good to a cat.

The most extraordinary difference between cats and humans is the cats' inability to taste sugars as sweet. They may not even be able to taste some sugars at all, but because some cats prefer sweetened to plain milk, it has been suggested that the addition of sugar can affect some other tastes. We can only imagine what such a change might be like, because our sensitivity to the sweetness of sugar would mask any more subtle effects, even if they were there. Perhaps we should envy the cat its obliviousness to this particular temptation, but this does not answer the question of why the cat does not taste sugars. The simple answer is that it does not need to; the foods that its body requires do not contain appreciable amounts of sugar, and a cat which ate large amounts of sweet things would miss out on many key nutrients. However, there is usually a reason why, during the course of evolution, a particular ability disappears completely. Since we cannot turn the clock back, it is impossible to say definitely what happened, but is probably significant that this loss of the ability to taste sugars is confined to the cats (most other carnivores, including dogs, have a sweet tooth). The cat responds not to sugars, but to amino-acids, which are the chemical building blocks of proteins. Some amino-acids, such as proline and lysine, do taste rather sweet to us, and these are the ones that cats prefer. Others, such as tryptophan, that taste bitter to us, are mostly rejected by cats, as are some related chemicals that gradually accumulate in the tissues of dead animals, which probably accounts for the dislike cats have for carrion. It is a reasonable guess that cats taste certain meats as sweet, and others as bitter, depending on which amino-acids are most abundant. During the early evolution of the cat family, the awareness of traces of sugars in the meats may have been a distraction from the important business of tasting the amino-acids,

(Opposite) Lucy and Calypso, two of the author's cats. Without even thinking about it, people can join the visible parts of the cats together to make two – psychologists have proved that cats can do this also.

and so the ability was lost.

The human sense of taste is traditionally broken down into four basic flavours; salt, bitter, sweet and sour. The cat seems to have little appreciation of salt, probably because it can get all it needs from food without making any special effort. Since plants tend to be deficient in salt, most plant-eating mammals have to have a very acute salt taste; this accounts for the passion that many of these animals have for salt licks. As we have established, cats do not consider sugars to be sweet, but they do recognize some amino-acids as sweet, and others as bitter. Alkaloids, which occur in many plants and taste bitter to us, also taste bitter to cats. The fourth flavour, sour, is generally disliked by cats. This flavour is usually produced by acids, like citric acid in lemons, but cats will refuse to eat foods that contain a related but distinct group of acids called medium-chain fatty acids. These are rarely found in meat, but are produced by some plants, and are found, for example, in coconut oil. Although people describe this as having a bland taste, cats loathe it; what seems to happen is that the cat's own saliva generates medium-chain fatty acids from the coconut oil while the oil is still in the cat's mouth, before it has a chance to swallow.

There are probably many more differences between ourselves and the cat in the way taste is perceived. Even the milk that queen cats produce for their kittens has a quite distinct composition, and therefore presumably a different taste, to cow's milk. We should not therefore be surprised that they like to eat things that we do not, and vice versa.

THE SENSES OF SMELL

This is not a misprint! Cats have not one, but two ways of detecting odours, one akin to our sense of smell, and one totally foreign to us. Smell is a mysterious sense to us; we are what scientists refer to as microsmic, which means we do not use our sense of smell very much. When we do, it is often at the subconscious level; smell is more closely connected to the emotions than any other sense. It is hard for us to imagine a world in which what an object smells like is more important than what it looks like, but this does not seem to present any problems to a cat. When your cat patrols the boundaries of your garden, it will stop suddenly and sniff intently at prominent, nose-height twigs. Presumably these have been scent-marked by another cat, perhaps not very long before. If that scent had come from the urine of an entire (i.e. unneutered) tom, we could (unwillingly!) share the experience of the aroma. On the other hand, it might have been marked by the cheek glands of a neutered female, the perfume from which has virtually no odour for us, yet it seems to speak volumes to another cat.

When cats lose their sense of smell through cat 'flu or some other infection, their behaviour can change dramatically. Some lose their appetite, some start to urinate indoors, and breeding females may lose their desire to court a male successfully. All of this tells us that odours are very important in the life of a cat. Partly because this world is mostly closed to us because of our lack of olfactory ability, we know very little about the smelly sensations that cats perceive.

Cats' greater sensitivity can be accounted for by the huge area of delicately folded membranes that carry the olfactory apparatus. Despite the small size of their heads, cats have five to ten times more olfactory epithelium, as these membranes are known, than we do. Beyond this, we can only guess as to how well, for example, they can discriminate between one faint aroma and another. Much more is known about the abilities of dogs, partly because it is easier to train them to demonstrate that they can tell the difference between one smell and another, and partly because of the uses to which we put the dog's nose. Dogs, being carnivores, like cats, may not be very much superior to cats in their olfactory abilities. The ability of the dog to tell people apart by their odours is legendary, but it can be fooled. It seems that, just as we can be confused by a pair of identical twins, so even the most discriminating of dogs may mistake the smell of one for the smell of the other, except when they are presented side-by-side and a direct choice is possible.

Another of the mysteries of feline smell begins as a small slit which can be seen just behind the upper incisor teeth. This is one end of the nasopalatine canal, the other end of which is in the nasal cavity. It is the opening of another olfactory organ, known as the vomeronasal or Jacobson's organ. This consists of two blind sacs, lying just above the roof of the mouth. These sacs are normally closed, and it is unlikely that they are used in ordinary

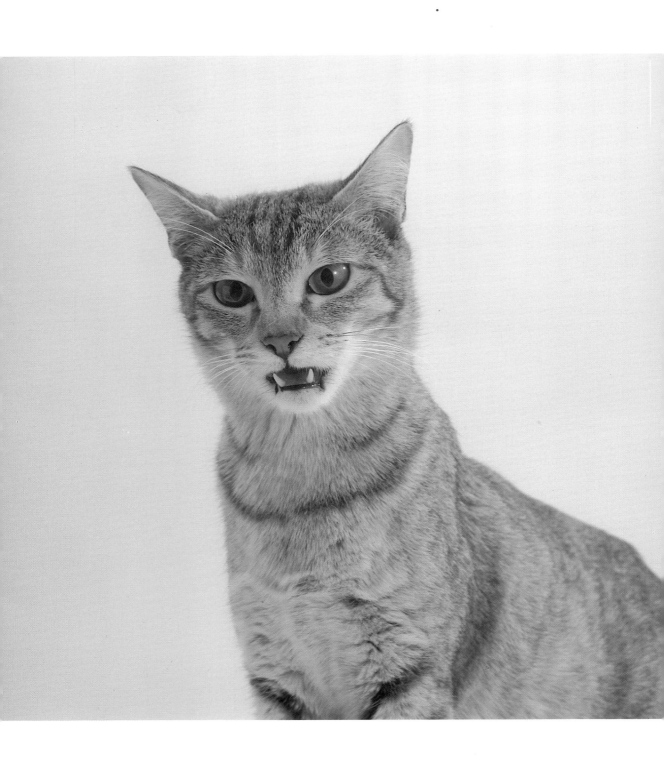

sniffing. Thus the cat, like ourselves, relies on its ordinary sense of smell for minute-to-minute checking of the air that it breathes.

So, when is the vomeronasal organ brought into play? Luckily, the cat gives a very obvious sign that this is happening. Only cat breeders are likely to have seen this, because it is mainly used as a part of the cat's sex life. In order to open the ducts to the sacs, the cat contorts its face, baring its upper teeth by raising its upper lip, and opening its mouth slightly. This gesture seems to have no commonly-accepted English name, and so is often known by the German word *Flehmen*. Receptive females will perform this to the odour of male urine, while males will "flehm" towards females themselves. The exact significance in courtship has not been fully investigated. In other mammals, such as hamsters, that have this organ, it has been shown that it is crucial to a successful first courtship, but that sexually experienced animals can fall back on their conventional sense of smell to judge the mood of their partner.

(Opposite) A female "flehming" after smelling the urine of a tom cat.

CHAPTER 3

What Your Cat Makes of the World

*M*ost cat owners think of their cats as being intelligent, and many go so far as to assume that cats are rational beings that can calculate their every move. It is tempting, and part of the fun of owning cats, to pretend that they are small, furry people that could probably talk to us if only their voice-boxes were the right shape, as the following excerpt, sampled virtually at random from the *Telegraph Magazine*, shows:

Edgar, our Maine Coon cat, and the mouse that lives in the dishwasher are still fencing with each other. Mrs Pam Morris writes from Leeds to ask if Edgar is not playing the game at which she caught her cat out. He was under marching orders for general dereliction of duty. Then he started to produce a live mouse for inspection on a daily basis. Eventually Mrs Morris detected that it was the same mouse, released at the end of the parade to ensure that the Morris household did not cut off cat rations. I wouldn't put it past Edgar – or the mouse. They are both living a fat and comfortable life while the drama continues.

The games that cats play are eternally fascinating and part of their charm. However, there is no logical basis for supposing that Mrs Morris' cat is conscious of what it is doing. The predatory behaviour of the domestic house cat is motivated and organized in such a way that not killing an animal that it has caught, although apparently illogical, is in fact natural and commonplace. Moreover, it is entirely feasible that Mrs Morris' favourable reaction to the first catching of the mouse helped to reinforce that part of the predatory sequence, and improve the probability that it would be repeated. Reinforcement, and the ways that cats can be trained, despite their unco-operative reputation, will be described later in this section.

This chapter will attempt to explain what we actually know about the mental abilities of cats. It has to be said from the outset that there is no good evidence for the idea that cats are conscious of their own actions, or can make reasoned decisions about their futures. However, that does not mean that biologists think that cats are stupid, or are in some general way inferior to people. The old arguments about whether such-and-such an animal is more or less intelligent than some other have been largely abandoned; they were largely fruitless anyway. Modern biologists are much more interested in how different species are adapted to their environments; cats are supreme experts at being cats, and should not be regarded as inferior human beings.

Because the cat's behaviour matches its domestic environment so well, it comes into fewer conflicts with humans when sharing their space than almost any other animal. This seems to be another reason for assuming that the cat is intelligent, but in all probability, the domestication of the cat was a lucky accident, on both sides of course. Just occasionally, the relative inflexibility of a cat's behaviour is shown up, as the following two examples should show.

When they are close to their core areas, cats usually bury their urine and faeces. As will be described in Chapter 6, this is as true of farmyard cats as it is of the pet that uses a litter tray or a convenient flowerbed. Litter trays are very effective, and

(Opposite) A lilac Burmese
gives the appearance of being
in ecstasy as it rolls in a bed
of catnip.

indispensable for the owner of a house-bound (usually apart-ment-bound) cat, but they are often too small to allow the cat to bury what it has just done, unless it chooses where to dig most carefully. It is commonplace to see a cat "digging" in thin air to one side of the tray, scooping imaginary grit backwards in exact-ly the right direction, but to no effect whatsoever. The burying of excreta consists of sets of complex reflexes, and although the cat will often sniff to see whether its digging has actually reduced the odour from its urine or faeces, there is no indication that it actually realizes that digging in litter works, while digging air does not. The whole operation proceeds on a hit-or-miss fashion until the end result is achieved (presumably, the odour becomes weaker than some pre-determined threshold), or the cat is dis-tracted by something else.

The other example of the cat giving itself away is its re-action to catnip. A cat will repeatedly rub its face on a catnip plant, and even roll on it; my own attempts to grow these plants in my garden have always ended in disaster, due to an over-enthusiastic nocturnal visitor smashing every one! This bizarre behaviour is induced by a number of chemicals with similar odours, one of which is found in catnip herbs, and others in a few otherwise unrelated plants such as the Japanese cat shrub, and the roots of the Chinese gooseberry, better known as the source of the kiwi fruit. Although these patterns of behaviour also form part of the courtship behaviour of entire (unneutered) females, entire (unneutered) males and neutered cats of both sexes perform them just as readily towards catnip. However, some cats show no reaction whatsoever, and it is now known that this inability is inherited. No real purpose for the behaviour has ever been suggested, and because not all cats do it, it is un-likely to be crucial to their survival. It seems to be a good example of the way that behaviour can be triggered by wholly accidental stimuli, and again there is no evidence for any purpose in the cat's behaviour. Presumably, the catnip reaction origi-nates in some fairly primitive feline behaviour, because lions and jaguars (but not tigers) perform their own version towards the same plants. Jaguars will roll on catnip-treated stones, rub their faces on them, and carry them around in their mouths. Lions not only do all of these, but become so playful that rough-and-tumble games break out spontaneously near to a source of catnip.

RHYTHMS OF LIFE

Cats are affected by internal clocks that change their responsiveness in a rhythmical way. These clocks are regulated in turn by the rhythms of the outside world; night and day, the seasons, and so on. The effects of these on the cat's behaviour are not well understood, although it is known that the amounts of certain hormones in the blood, including the "fight or flight" hormone adrenaline, tend to be higher at certain times of the year and lower at others.

The internal rhythm that has most effect on our lives is our sleep-wake cycle, which in most people would repeat in just over twenty-four hours if left to its own devices, but is reset every day by cues from the environment, chiefly daylight. A very similar rhythm, also just over twenty-four hours long, can be detected in cats, but their sleep-wake cycles are much more flexible than ours, and can be highly individual. Most cats sleep several times in every twenty-four hours; it is perfectly natural for a well-fed carnivore to spend a considerable amount of time resting or sleeping. Unlike herbivores, which have to feed for many hours each day to obtain enough nourishment to live on, carnivores have opted for a more unpredictable but nutritionally much more concentrated type of food. If this proves hard to come by, long hours of hunting may be required. If it is easy to obtain – and what could be easier than waiting for one's doting owner to dish out some tasty morsel from the supermarket – then sleeping in between meals is a sensible strategy, and minimizes energy expenditure and the potentially dangerous attentions of predators or quarrelsome cats.

In a sense, the natural state of the cat is one of sleep, because there is a structure within the brain, called the reticular formation, whose activity keeps it awake. This control centre is stimulated in turn by input from the senses, and also hunger and thirst, all ensuring that the cat stays awake when it needs to eat or drink or pay attention to some excitement. Assuming that none of these apply, and the cat has dropped off, after a while it may begin to twitch in its sleep, giving every indication that it is dreaming. The trick to find out whether people are dreaming when in this state is to wake them quickly, and in the vast majority of cases they then report dreams. Cats cannot, of course, tell us whether or not they remember a dream, but it is possible to measure their brainwaves while they are asleep, to see if they go through changes similar to ours as sleep progresses. This can be done simply and without causing the cat any discomfort, by attaching a few detectors to the skin on the head.

When a cat is awake, the electroencephalographs (EEGs) that are produced show all sorts of low intensity, high frequency changes, which must depend on what information from the outside the brain is processing at the time. As the cat falls asleep, and the sensory systems are put on standby, so the brain adopts its own independent rhythms. For the first ten minutes to half an hour, the EEG becomes deeper and slower; during this light sleep the cat can be woken easily. If the sleeping bout continues, a further change in the EEG occurs. High frequency patterns return, superficially rather like the patterns recorded during the waking state, but the cat is actually harder to wake during this phase than in the previous one; for this reason this phase is often referred to as paradoxical sleep. The main muscles of the body and legs become completely limp, except when a few of them contract suddenly to produce the twitch of a paw or tail. The eyes may move and the whiskers may twitch, as if some imaginary prey were being chased. Human EEGs associated with dreaming sleep are similar to those of the cat's paradoxical sleep, and all the evidence points to a cat's dream being real.

Young kittens spend 60 to 70 per cent of their time asleep, this proportion declining from three weeks of age. For the first couple of weeks, kittens may dream all the time that they are asleep, because their EEGs are full of activity. Light, non-dreaming sleep appears gradually, until by the seventh or eighth week kittens sleep like adult cats.

REFLEX BEHAVIOUR

While it is obviously beneficial for a cat to use its brainpower in many situations, there are some circumstances when the brain is just too slow to deliver an effective response. The ways that the balance organs are connected to a whole battery of reflexes have been discussed. Other reflexes produce scratching, the basic walking movements of the legs, hissing, growling, tail-lashing and the baring of claws. Many so-called reflexes involve the brain to a degree, but nevertheless occur very rapidly.

Sleep – a cat's natural state.

One of these is the orienting reflex, which is used when a cat turns its head quickly towards a sudden noise. Apart from the position in which the head ends up, the different elements of this reflex are more or less fixed. At the same time as the movement, the eyes are automatically focussed on a point about 15 cm (6 in) from the face. This occurs even if the stimulus is actually much further away, and illustrates the pre-programmed nature of the response. Since a sudden event close to the cat is likely to be more immediately dangerous than one that occurs far away, it presumably pays to check the immediate environment first, and then relax the eyes to look further away. Other aspects of the reflex are equally rigidly programmed, including the factors that trigger it. Flashes of light produce the same reaction as loud noises, and it is the novelty of the stimulus that is most important. For example, a sound that increases in volume gradually may not induce the orienting reflex until it is suddenly cut off. Stimuli that are repeated exactly over and over again quickly lose their ability to induce the reflex, although they may lead to other, more "considered" reactions. However, for a while immediately after the reflex occurs the cat becomes more attentive, due to changes in the flow of blood through its brain.

The capture of prey is another critical occasion when reactions have to be as fast as possible. Around its mouth, from the hairless skin of the nose to just beyond the bases of its whiskers, the cat has receptors under its skin. As soon as any part of this area contacts the surface of the prey, the precise point of contact

A cat about to bite is guided by touch receptors on the skin around its mouth, in the shaded areas.

is relayed to the reflex which twists the head around to ready the jaws for their killing bite. The next set of receptors lie along both lips, and when these are contacted in the right way the jaws open wide. The bite itself is triggered by a third set of receptors just inside the mouth, and may be steered by yet more receptors at the bases of the long canine teeth. This deadly set of reflexes occurs almost instantaneously, and is perhaps the most graphic demonstration of the wild side of the cat.

However, these are not automatic reflexes that occur willy-nilly. They are normally inhibited by the brain, and are only switched on by the sight and possibly smell of prey, and the cat's general state of excitement when it is moving in for the kill. A gentle touch on the side of the mouth from an owner's hand will usually produce no more from the cat than a gentle movement of the head, that probably serves to deposit scents from its oral glands. This tremendous flexibility and appropriateness of response is a characteristic of the behaviour of mammals, but it should not be taken as proof of conscious thought on the cat's part.

THE CAT'S BRAIN

Brain-power has undoubtedly been a major force in the evolution of the modern cat family. The reason why one extinct arm of the cat family, the paleofelids, died out about seven million years ago, was most probably an increase in the size and complexity of the brain in the modern cats, the neofelids. We know this because it is possible to make casts from the inside of skulls, not just from museum specimens of current species, but also from fossils of both living and extinct ones. Sometimes the changes that have taken place are rather difficult to interpret; the sabre-tooth cats provide one example. One group of sabretooths that died out only a few million years ago had an essentially modern felid brain, but with some unusual features. It is a problem to disentangle which of these features reflect changes in the way the brain works, and which were forced on the brain by changes in the skull, needed to accommodate the massive canine teeth and jaw muscles. However, the feline brain does not seem to have evolved very much over the past ten million years. In other words, a lion's brain is essentially similar to a domestic cat's brain.

Of course, they are hugely different in size, but does that make the lion more intelligent? The short answer is, not necessarily, because a large body has a large amount of skin which requires large numbers of touch receptors, and large muscles which need large numbers of nerves to control them. It is possible to estimate how much of the brain is likely to be required for these and other basic functions, and then calculate the proportion left over for more sophisticated processing of information. The extent to which each species' brain is larger or smaller than expected has been given the name "encephalization quotient", or EQS for short, by Professor Harry Jerison of the University of California in Los Angeles. A high EQ need not reflect intelligence alone; it may be required to cope with some particularly demanding facet of the animal's lifestyle. For example, animals that fly, or swim underwater, seem to need larger brains than those that live on the surface of the ground, both because they need to make more complex movements, and because they need to scan their environment from all angles, down as well as up. Animals that run from predators, and therefore need to detect them from a distance, often have larger brains than those that rely on passive defence. Social life, even if it only amounts to the mother looking after the young until they are mature, also demands an increase in brain-power. One of the lowest EQs possessed by any mammal belongs to the hedgehog; it lives on the ground, has little social life, and simply rolls into a ball when threatened. The apes have high EQs, reflecting not only their superior learning abilities, but also the complexity of their social lives.

The cat family all have rather similar EQs, with the exception, for some unknown reason, of the lynx. The EQs are about average for a carnivorous mammal; the greatest enlargement of the brain among the carnivores is found among some of the dog family. Part of the reason for this difference is that there is a much larger olfactory bulb in dogs than in cats; as its name implies, this part of the brain is mainly concerned with processing information about odours. It would in fact be difficult for a cat to fit a much larger olfactory bulb into its short, flat-faced skull. The dog family, many of which hunt by scent, seem to have an extraordinarily well-developed sense of smell. A cat's is probably just about average for a mammal, which is to say much better than a human's. However, this difference in sensory ability cannot account for the whole difference in brain size, and it has been suggested that the complex social behaviour of some canids, like the wolf, also requires extra brain-power. This is reflected in the wolf's very rich repertoire of social behaviour, which includes a complex set of signals indicating submission to the most dominant individuals in the pack.

Much of the domestic cat's brain is devoted to its athletic, not to say balletic, abilities. The cerebellum, the part that co-ordinates balance and movement, is much larger than in other mammals, and a large part of the cortex is devoted to controlling movement. Also in the cortex is a large area devoted to the processing of huge amounts of information generated by the cat's sensitive ears (*see Chapter 2*).

INTELLIGENCE

Cats can impress us one minute with their cunning, and exasperate us the next when they seem incapable of understanding something that seems blindingly obvious. How many of us have shouted out "Oh, you stupid cat!", and yet at the same time we are proud of our cat's intelligence. This paradox arises because of our self-centred notions of what intelligence is. In many ways, cats are not as clever as people, but they are capable of doing some things that we are not. Take the example of a cat lost, or abandoned by its owner, and therefore denied access to regular food and shelter. Many such cats adapt almost instantly to catching or scrounging their own food, and finding a warm, dry place to sleep, and can survive in this semi-wild way until, hopefully, they find a new home. Could we suddenly adapt to living off the land in this way?

So what is it that makes cats think differently to the way that we do? As already mentioned, the old-fashioned idea that all species could be placed on a scale from the most stupid to the most intelligent has been abandoned. All types of animals have evolved to live in a particular way in a particular part of the world, and to date no other animal has bettered them at that. If they had, the inferior species would have been replaced by the superior, and would probably have become extinct. So, in this sense, all species are successes, and it is wrong to think of one as being superior to another just because it has more human-like intelligence. Nowadays, psychologists interested in animals talk about "ecologically surplus abilities", which reflect how adaptable a species is likely to be when faced with an unusual situation. Some species seem to be so well tuned to their environment that they may be incapable of much change, certainly within a single lifetime. Others, notably animals like the apes or the dolphins, can learn all sorts of new skills to cope with new challenges.

The cat lies somewhere between these two extremes. As a specialized carnivore, the things that it is most capable of learning seem to be limited by the changes it is likely to encounter. This can be illustrated by the way that cats and rats respond differently to a simple learning experiment, where the animal is placed in a long but rather narrow chamber, with a loudspeaker at one end and a food dispenser at the other. The arrival of food in the dispenser is signalled by a ten-second burst of clicking sounds from the loudspeaker. Rats quickly learn that the noise means that food will appear, and after a few repetitions will rush to the dispenser as soon as they hear the sound. Cats have a great difficulty in learning that a sound in one place means food in another. They tend to run towards the loudspeaker, away from the food, and attack it as if prey was concealed behind it. Sounds are so important to a hunting cat that it is difficult to break the association between the direction of a sound and the direction of a food item. Rats, as opportunistic scavengers, seem to have little difficulty in learning that a noise in one place means food in another. That is not to say, however, that rats are "smarter" than cats. The cat's EQ is higher, and there are many other learning situations that rats find very difficult to master. It is just that the cat is a hunter, and is most able to learn things that are likely to be useful in hunting.

Before going on to look at intelligence in more detail, it is worthwhile to consider the most basic forms of learning, processes that many animals use to build up a reliable picture of the way the world around them is constructed, and how to deal with it. These abilities are shared by animals as simple as caterpillars, and as complex as ourselves, but that is no reason to dismiss them as trivial. Similar processes go on in our brains all the time, although we are usually unaware of them, because by and large they operate at a subconscious level.

<u>LEARNING HOW THE WORLD FITS TOGETHER</u>

Many kinds of animals, particularly simple ones, probably never learn to recognize one another as individuals. They may be able to distinguish members of their own species from others, they may be able to gauge some of their characteristics, such as how strong they appear to be, but they never *know* one another in our meaning of the word. This might not present too many difficulties to a cat that lives wild in the outback of Australia, rarely coming into contact with other cats. However, many cats lead complex social lives, and anyone who has kept several cats together is unlikely to need much convincing that they do know each other as individuals.

Any idea that cats are born with detailed knowledge of the cats around them can be dismissed as impossible, so recognition of individuals must be based upon learning. The process that enables stimuli that occur together to be linked is known as Pavlovian learning, named after Ivan Pavlov and his famous experiments with dogs. Dogs have remained among the favourite subjects for this kind of study ever since, but since dogs and cats are close relatives, we can assume that they have very similar capabilities, particularly at such a relatively unsophisticated level of learning.

Pavlov trained his dogs to associate the arrival of food with a stimulus that he provided himself, such as the sound of a buzzer. The smell of the food would cause the dogs to salivate spontaneously; if the buzzer was sounded every time that the food arrived, the dogs would salivate every time they heard the sound of the buzzer, whether or not there was any food in the vicinity. While it is reasonable to assume that dogs are born with the ability to tell what some foods smell like, the sound of the buzzer is artificial and has to be learned by the dog. There has been a great deal of discussion about what has actually been learned under these circumstances. Is it the sound itself that triggers the response, or does the sound conjure up some "idea" of food, and then the "idea" triggers the response? Most psychologists now think that the latter is more likely. I have put the word "idea" in inverted commas, because it is not necessary for any conscious picture of the food to be produced for the process to work, even in people.

In the past, psychologists tended to emphasize the

arbitrary nature of the learned stimulus, and the naturalness of the original one. It is now known that two arbitrary stimuli can also take place without the cat having to make any actual response. For example, a cat in unfamiliar surroundings will observe and learn about them even before it has started to explore. It is also clear that animals learn some associations quickly, while others are very difficult to learn. One example of this, the problems that cats have learning that a sound in one place means food in another, has already been mentioned. Each species seems to have preset guidelines that help it to learn things that fit in with the way it lives. It is also known now that animals do not behave like robots, but have some flexibility of response to the stimuli, provided that the responses are alternatives linked together by what are called motivational systems. These usually correspond to some aspect of the cat's life, such as hunger, thirst, attack, defence or mating. Each will exert control over a whole range of responses, and the one that is expressed will depend on the situation as the cat sees it. Young male cats are frequently threatened with attack by the adult toms within a social group, and quickly learn which toms to avoid. However, what they actually do depends on the circumstances. If they spot the tom first, they may "freeze" in an attempt to avoid detection. If the tom is on top of them before they see him, then flight is the only course of action left.

This type of learning rarely happens instantaneously; the most glaring exception is the learning that takes place when a food turns out to be toxic, which will be discussed in the next chapter. The reason for this is obvious; all sorts of coincidences occur in the life of a cat, and if every single one was learned immediately, the cat's head would soon become stuffed with misinformation that was indistinguishable from real information. Therefore, two stimuli have to occur several times, either simultaneously or virtually so, before they are learned. If one occurs only sometimes, and the other also occurs on its own, then learning is delayed even more. Any mistakes can be corrected by a kind of "unlearning". Two stimuli that always occurred together, but then change, quickly become dissociated again. If you shake a box every time you give your cat dry food, it will learn that the sound means food (this can be a useful trick for getting your cat indoors at night, if you want to shut it in). If you switch to shaking the box every time you see the cat, *except* when you are about to feed it, the original response wanes rapidly. While this is going on, you may of course get other responses that can loosely be ascribed to frustration on the cat's part!

STUDYING THE CAT'S ABILITIES

Pavlovian learning is a useful way of simplifying the world and making it more meaningful, but it relies upon pre-existing skills. Instrumental learning allows animals to refine those actions that

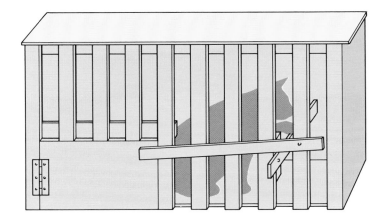

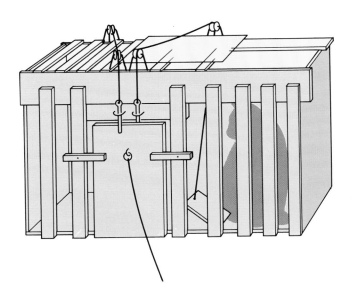

Two of the puzzle boxes devised by Edward Thorndike to test the learning abilities of cats. The box shown above was relatively easy to open: a simple push downwards on the bar inside the box would raise the latch and allow the door to open. The one below is more complicated: the cat has to perform three separate tasks, one by treading on the small platform, one by clawing at the string on the left through the bars of the roof, and one by turning either of the wooden catches on the door itself. The door then falls away, pulled by a counterweight (not shown) on the other end of the string attached to the middle of the door.

produce results, and discard those that do not. Again, this is most easily demonstrated in situations which are very unlikely to have featured in the evolution of the cat, and are therefore unlikely to have their origins in instinct. Psychologists first began to study such abilities in cats about the turn of the century. One of the first was Edward Thorndike, who devised increasingly cunning puzzle-boxes from which his subjects were encouraged to escape. Escape was always within the capabilities of the cats, provided they could work out the correct responses, and if unsuccessful, they were always released after a while. However, most of his cats learned the simple puzzles, and some learned the complicated ones (*see diagram on previous page*). Because on average the cats took less and less time to escape each time they repeated the same puzzle, Thorndike concluded that the learning took place gradually.

L.T. Hobhouse, Professor of Sociology at the University of London during the First World War, used a different experimental approach, one that these days we would think of as being more humane than Thorndike's. The notes he took of his experiments bring them to life in a way that modern scientific accounts seldom do, and also give an insight into the joys and frustrations of trying to work out what a cat is thinking.

> My first experiment was with my cat Tim, a small black tom, rather more than a year old. . . . Tim is a sociable creature, who follows his friends about in the half dog-like way that some cats have, but as a psychologist he has two great defects. His attention is of the most fickle order, and what is even worse, he gets his meals at the most irregular times, and by methods known only to himself. It is therefore impossible to say beforehand whether he will take any sustained interest in the proceedings at all.

Many of Hobhouse's experiments consisted of simple puzzles that his animals had to solve to obtain a small piece of food.

> A piece of meat was placed on a card to which a string was tied, and then placed on a shelf beyond reach of the animal with the string dangling down . . . . I first tried this with

Tim, thinking that a young cat would very likely pull the string in play. I was surprised to find that he took no notice of it. I showed him seven times, pulling the string down before his eyes, and letting him get the meat. Neither this, nor a series of trials in which the card was placed on the table barely out of the cat's reach, had the slightest effect. The kitten once grabbed the string as I was arranging the card, probably in play, and brought the card down without the meat. For the rest, he either made no attempt at all, or tried to claw at the meat directly.

About a fortnight afterwards I began a long series of trials in which the string was tied to a chair leg to make it more conspicuous. . . . Fourteen trials gave no result. Next day, eight trials passed without result, but at the ninth, the cat bit slightly at the string close by my fingers as I adjusted it, and as soon as I had got it right, pawed the string down. The biting was doubtless due to the string being slightly smeared with fish, but the effect was apparently to call the cat's attention to the string for the first time in all this long series. It is clear that, in pawing it, his aim was to get the fish on the table. If he had merely been attracted by the smear on the string, he would have used his mouth. At the next trial, he sat still for a while, and then pawed the string again. At the next, he took to washing himself, and I gave up for a time; but on replacing the string I saw him watching me, and he pulled it down at once. In the next trial he did the same.

Next day he appeared to have forgotten, but walked under the string and knocked it down with his tail. At the second trial, he slightly brushed against the string, but walked away. I had to rearrange it. He watched me doing so, and pawed it down at once. He then pulled it five times running without hesitation.

Although he does not actually say so, one gets the impression from reading this passage that Hobhouse almost felt that the cat was treating the whole exercise as a game, a sentiment shared by any cat owner that tries to get their cat to do something it does not want to do. This cat's repeated failure to understand what was expected of it can be interpreted in at least two ways.

One is that the cat had difficulty in recognizing the thin string as a relevant cue, a situation possibly made worse by its long sight (*see the previous chapter*). The other, which puts the cat in a better light, is based on the lack of reward when he first pulled the card down. Having failed to deliver anything more interesting than a piece of card on that crucial first occasion, the string became uninteresting, until, much later, his attention was drawn back to it by the smell of the fish. Whichever is true, both point to very rapid perfection of the task once the cat had begun to learn it. Because such a process immediately makes us draw a parallel with a flash of inspiration of our own, it is tempting to use this as evidence for rational thought in the cat. However, there is no reason why important consequences, such as obtaining food, should not promote the rapid acquisition of skills. After all, a kitten born in the wild has just a few weeks to turn from being completely dependent on its mother into a competent hunter, or it will not survive.

There are some other clues that might suggest that the cat is not really thinking about what it is doing. For example, Thorndike found that his cats could never learn to escape from one of his boxes by accidentally dislodging the latch with their tails, however many times they repeated it. You or I would quickly realize that the latch always went down when our backs were turned, and then probably conclude that escape had something to do with our (hypothetical!) tails. Cats never seem to make that kind of connection. They are also hidebound by the sorts of actions that they use instinctively, for example in hunting. Thorndike found that it was easy to train a cat to hook a bolt back with its claw, the kind of movement used by a hunting cat to fish its prey out from a crevice. The same cats found it much harder to learn that a bolt had to be pushed away from them, something that is perfectly feasible for a cat to do, but not a movement common in hunting behaviour.

CATS *CAN* BE TRAINED

Dogs, porpoises, even killer whales are easily trained, but cats? There are probably several reasons why the trained cat is such a rarity. One is that there is no real need to train a cat to turn it into a rewarding companion, whereas all dogs require a minimal

(Above) With perseverance, cats can be trained to perform simple tricks.

amount of training to make sure that they are at least controllable. Another is the general inactivity of the adult cat – most of the time it does not do very much, so opportunities for training are limited. Thirdly, cats rarely respond to praise in the way that dogs do. Dogs seem to regard their owners as dominant members of their "pack", and can be rewarded simply with affectionate social contact. What cats may or may not see in us is discussed in Chapter 8, but a stroke or a pat do not seem to be sufficiently motivating to train a desired response.

Highly palatable food is the only reward that is commonly used for training cats. Kittens have been trained using exploration of a novel environment as a reward, but there are obvious practical difficulties in adapting this for use at home, and a favourite dry cat food is often the most convenient way of rewarding a cat for a correct response.

It seems to be difficult to get cats to perform very unusual tricks; the response from the cat is usually something from its normal repertoire, and the "trick" is involved in producing it to order. In the training, the technique of shaping can be used to single out the desired response, even if it is rarely performed spontaneously by the cat. The cat is first rewarded for some behaviour pattern that resembles, or contains some component of, the pattern that is the ultimate goal of the training. The signal could be, for example, a spoken command. The most effective reinforcement comes when the reward is offered to the cat within one second of its performing the required response; any delay and learning is slowed down considerably. Gradually, the cat will begin to respond on cue, and then only the ultimate response is rewarded, until the cat only performs that response. Maintenance of the trick is most effective when the reward is only offered occasionally, after several correct performances, and at unpredictable intervals. Shaping is effective on a wide range of animals, and is extensively used for all kinds of training.

Cats can be taught to jump over a stick in this way. Both dogs and cats will naturally leap over obstacles, but a dog can be trained quite quickly to expect praise from its owner whenever it jumps. The average cat would simply walk round the stick (if it had not already walked off in some other direction) and so the trick has to be built up in stages. First of all, the stick is placed on the ground, and the cat is simply rewarded whenever it walks over it. After a few sessions, a smart cat will begin to divert from its normal path in order to pass over the stick, provided it has previously been rewarded *immediately* after its fourth paw is across. Once this has been established, the stick can be raised up off the ground very slightly, just before the cat reaches it. If it then steps over the stick, a reward is given; if it does not, there is no reward.

Scolding incorrect responses will almost certainly put the cat off the whole idea, so only positive reinforcement should be given. Gradually, the height of the stick can be raised, until only leaps are rewarded. Once the leap is high enough to make a convincing trick (not too high, or the cat will be tempted to walk underneath), it will persist for much longer if the reward is only provided for every third or fourth correct response. However, if there is any sign that the cat's response is waning, it should be

put back on to continuous reinforcement, in other words rewarded for every correct response, until the trick is reliable
once more.

More complex tricks, or ones that require the cat to be out
of reach of the owner when the response is performed, often
rely on what is called second order reinforcement. This is used
extensively for training sea mammals like porpoises, because
the trainer standing on the side of the pool cannot immediately
reinforce a response that is happening underwater; by the time
the porpoise has surfaced and can be offered fish, too much time
will have elapsed since the trick was performed for the reward to
be effective. First of all, a Pavlovian connection has to be established to show the animal that food always follows some arbitrary
signal from the trainer, say a snap of the fingers or, for the porpoises, a click from an underwater loudspeaker. No response
has yet been trained, but now the snap of the fingers can be used
as the reward, since it conjures up some image of food in the
animal's mind.

In this way a cat can be taught to retrieve. Something suitable, like a miniature dumb-bell, is slightly smeared in food to
attract the cat's attention. As soon as the cat touches it with its
mouth, the trainer snaps her fingers, and as soon as possible
thereafter, gives the cat its expected food reward. The same
shaping technique can be used to mould this response into a
proper retrieve, and even fancy twists, such as the cat dropping
the dumb-bell into a particular bowl, can be added if the trainer is
really dedicated. Apart from strict adherence to presenting the
rewards for the right responses at the right moments, the main
quality required is an unusual degree of patience from the
trainer!

Tricks that consist of complex chains of behaviour are best
trained backwards rather than forwards. First of all the last component is trained; once it is established, it appears to become
rewarding in its own right, and the animal can be trained to perform the one-from-last part of the trick using the last part as the
reward, provided the food is still provided at the end. In this
way, quite complex sequences, of the sort that were once very
popular in circuses, can be built up. Because of the relative difficulty of establishing even simple tricks in cats, these behaviour
chains are much more commonly taught to dogs.

CAN TRAINING BE USED TO CURE BEHAVIOURAL PROBLEMS?

Treatment of so-called "problem behaviours" in dogs often involves elements of training, sometimes just for the dog but often for the owner as well! Cats are generally less likely than dogs to be taken by their owners for behavioural counselling, and the remedies tend to rely on the adaptation of the cat's instinctive behaviour, rather than attempting to modify it by training. For example, indoor urination usually stems from an alteration in the cat's normal territorial behaviour. The installation of a cat flap is often the trigger, either because the home cat's perception of "outdoors" and "indoors" become blurred, or because intruding cats damage the resident's sense of security. The first step in treatment in such cases should be to board up the flap! What should never be done is to punish the cat, particularly after the unwanted event has occurred. As was described above, cats and most other animals associate unpleasant consequences, such as being scolded or shoo-ed out of the house, with the event that immediately preceded it. This will almost certainly be the appearance on the scene of the owner, so the punishment becomes associated with the owner, not the urination. Thus the cat becomes less attached to its home environment, and further indoor urine-marking is almost inevitable. However, a very mild form of aversion can be used to train confident cats not to do certain things that seem to be particularly tempting. A short, well-aimed squirt of water from a plant sprayer, particularly if it is held at arms' length, will often catch a cat unawares, and if not over-used, need not be associated with the owner. I have used this technique to good effect to deter my cats from playing with the Christmas tree! Digging up the compost about house-plants can reportedly be deterred by a strategically placed, cocked but upside-down, mousetrap.

Positive associations can also be used, for example to improve the bond between cat and owner. An under-attached, nervous cat can be trained by feeding it small, frequent meals; immediately before each meal the owner should talk to it in a calm, gentle way. Once this routine has been established, positive associations between food and handling can be built up, starting with gentle touching of the cat's back; the area immediately in front of the tail seems to be particularly effective. A complementary approach based on instinctive behaviour can also be used; owners who approach their cats on all fours and attempt the human equivalent of the head-rubbing display (*see Chapter 6*) are often rewarded by intense rubbing and purring from the cat.

The above is merely intended to illustrate some of the ways that the cat's capacity to learn can be used to cement the bond between cat and owner. Treatment of serious problem behaviour is a professional task. Luckily it is now possible to obtain help in the U.K. and parts of Europe from members of the Association of Pet Behaviour Counsellors, who can be contacted through your vet.

FELINE INTELLIGENCE

It is no longer fashionable to study feline intelligence. To psychologists, the cat's intransigence makes it an awkward subject, and so recent writings on the mental abilities of the cat have tended towards the fanciful, recounting unsubstantiated stories that purport to "prove" that cats have psychic powers. Many of the cat's supposedly supernatural abilities can be explained straightforwardly, in terms of the superior sensory abilities described in the last chapter. Tales of cats that travel huge distances to be reunited with their owners conveniently omit to mention just how rare such events are. Millions of cats worldwide go missing every year and are never found; some of the few that do trace their owners probably do so by coincidence, and some may simply be cases of mistaken identity.

Rather than speculating about one-off events, it is more revealing of cats' natures to discover their true capabilities, and what kind of information they can extract from their world. Most of the experimental work that has been done tests the way that things look to cats. They can presumably process data coming from sounds and smells in similar ways, but given that both of these senses are more sensitive than vision, their mental abilities in these areas may be more sophisticated than we yet know.

We can tell that cats form simple "concepts" about what they see, by training them to respond to the appearance of particular objects, and then testing to see whether other objects are recognized as similar. For example, it has been shown in this

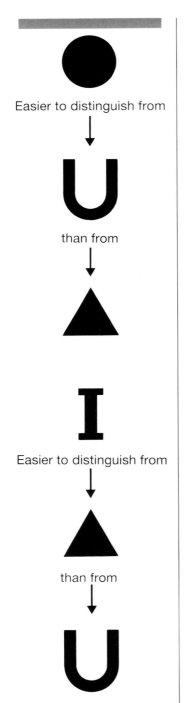

Easier to distinguish from

↓

than from

↓

Easier to distinguish from

↓

than from

↓

way that cats can judge the relative sizes of two objects. If trained to respond to the larger object out of otherwise similar pairs, they will still pick out the larger one, even when the size of both is increased so that the small object is now larger than the original large object. Shapes also have a meaning of their own, since a black-on-white version of a particular shape, say a triangle, is recognized as similar to a white-on-black triangle.

Several features of a figure can be learned at once; for example, a cat trained to respond to black rectangles will also pick out another black figure compared to a white one, and to a rectangle of any colour, if the alternative is neither a rectangle nor black. Rats tend to "latch on" to one feature or the other, say the black colour, and then pick out only black objects. Cats are also much less likely than rodents to get confused when picking out the relevant features from a jumbled sequence of cues, some rewarded and some not. For example, an individual cat could be rewarded for picking out the triangle from a pair consisting of a triangle and a circle. To make the task harder, there could be four examples of each shape, two large, two small, and each size black or white. The first pair might be a large black triangle, with food concealed underneath, and a small white circle. Is the most important feature the colour, the shape or the size? The cat finds the food, and seems to remember them all (triangle, black, large). The next pair is a small black triangle, concealing the reward, and a large white circle. This rules out large size as the cue, so it must be either black or triangular objects that indicate the location of food. The next pair, small white triangle, rewarded, and large black circle, unrewarded, theoretically clinches the solution, although in real trials cats may make some errors. However, even in a complex set of discriminations like these, cats learn the correct solution almost as quickly as when the relevant cue is presented on its own, say large black triangle against large black circle. Most of the mistakes that cats make seem to stem from their single-mindedness; they often persist with an original and seemingly arbitrary preference (in the example just discussed, perhaps for circles) even when it should be patently obvious that responses to circles do not lead to rewards.

The examples described above can be perfected by most cats; some, but perhaps not all, cats can make more sophisticated distinctions. For example, it is well established that chimpanzees can learn the concept of the odd one out in a group of three. Two identical objects, for example two cones, and one dissimilar object, for example a cube, are presented and selection of the cube is rewarded. The objects are changed randomly to prevent an association building up between a particular type of object and the reward. Chimpanzees quickly learn to pick the odd one, even when both of the pair are identical to the object rewarded on the previous occasion. Some cats never learn this distinction, although some do, and it may simply be that for the ones that do not, shape is just not an important enough cue.

CAN CATS COUNT, OR TELL THE TIME?

Anyone who has bred cats will have seen the obvious distress of a mother cat whose kitten has disappeared, and will probably have jumped to the conclusion that the mother has counted her kittens, and found she is one short. This is not the only explanation, however; it is more likely that by the time they are several weeks old, she knows each one by its smell, by what it looks like, and possibly by the noises it makes. The idea that she counts her litter, like a schoolteacher on a class outing, seems less feasible. Yet cats do seem to have some vague idea of number, provided the numbers are smaller than seven. Quite what they might use this ability for is unknown.

A sense of time might be more useful; for example, a hunting cat could tell not only that it was feeling hungry at a particular instant, but also "realize" that this was because it had been hunting in an unproductive area for too long. Cats can distinguish between sounds of different duration – for example, a tone lasting four seconds from one lasting five – so they must have an internal clock that can be used like a simple timer.

THE SEARCH FOR A HIDDEN OBJECT

Picture a cat watching a mouse through a window. The mouse disappears completely behind a tree-trunk. Since one is indoors and the other outdoors, the mouse cannot be heard or smelt by

(Opposite) The most important feature of a shape, so far as cats are concerned, seems to be how complex its outline is. They tend to make most mistakes when discriminating between two simple shapes, say a disc and a solid triangle, or between two complicated shapes with concave angles, such as the letters U and I. What they seem to concentrate on best is the ratio between an object's surface area and how convoluted its outline is.

the cat. To begin with, the cat concentrates on the point at which the mouse disappeared, and then gradually seems to lose interest. Does the cat remember the mouse once it can see it no longer? Is it able to guess where the mouse might have gone? Such mental skills would obviously be useful to a hunter, but that does not necessarily mean that the cat is capable of them.

This concept of "object permanence" has been studied in humans, since it can be seen to develop from early on in infants. The Swiss psychologist Jean Piaget devised a six-point scale to quantify the development of the response, and this is a useful way of comparing cats' abilities with those of children. There is no doubt that cats are more developed than the first two stages, in which very young infants show little interest in objects that are moved, or if they do, stare at the place in which they last saw them, rather than where they might be. In stage three, an object retains its identity even when it is partly hidden. Stage four introduces the simplest form of object permanence; an object that disappears stimulates a search, but the search follows some pre-determined pattern, possibly starting where the object is most often found. In stage five, the child or cat has to deduce what has happened from what it has just seen. For example, an object is hidden in several places in turn, but is visible in between. A child at stage four might look in each of the hiding-places in turn, but one at stage five would go straight to the last one. Children at stage six can solve the more difficult problem of following an object between hiding-places, when it is *not* visible in between.

There has been some argument as to whether cats reach stage six, or get stuck at stage five. One problem is to find something that interests the cat so much that it will ignore the novelty value of investigating everything in sight. The best way of keeping the subject's attention is to hide pieces of a favourite dry cat food. Given that cats have refined noses, it is always difficult to eliminate the possibility that they find hidden food from its smell, or even traces of the smell if the food has been surreptitiously removed. These experiments also betray a human's vision-centred view of the world. As we have seen, cats rely much more on hearing than on vision to locate prey when hunting in thick cover, so we may be underestimating their abilities by giving them tests devised specifically for humans.

HOW CATS FIND THEIR WAY AROUND

Most cats are real home-lovers, and get progressively more nervous the further they get from their base. On moving a cat to a new home, it is advisable to keep it indoors for the first two or three weeks, in case its temporary insecurity causes it to run away. We tend to assume that cats learn their environment by its appearance, as we do, but the smell of their surroundings must be just as important. This morning I parked my car in the street, a little way from my house, instead of pulling it up on to the driveway. Glancing out of the window, I saw Splodge, my long-haired neutered tom, sniffing the front number-plate intently. Every ten seconds or so he made as it to move away, but then returned for a further bout of sniffing. When the car is parked in the drive, he regularly rubs his cheek along that number-plate, and other cats in the neighbourhood may also from time to time. His surprise at finding that smell moved along 20 m (66 ft) seemed real.

Unfortunately, orientation by odour has hardly been studied in cats; our human-centred view of the world has meant that researchers have concentrated on unravelling the mysteries of how cats use visual landmarks. Much of the time, a pet cat will be in totally familiar surroundings, and able to see where it wants to go, either directly or through the use of landmarks. For example, a cat sitting on a windowsill knows that, when it has crossed the room to the doorway, it will have to turn, say, right, to get to its cat-flap. The appearance of the doorway might act as a simple cue, "switching on" the right turn. This kind of rather robot-like orientation is used by animals such as wasps and ants, that have much simpler brains than the cat's. Niko Tinbergen, one of the founding fathers of the science of animal behaviour, performed some early but elegant experiments with sand-wasps which clearly illustrate the drawbacks of relying on a simple system. While each sand-wasp was out of sight in its burrow, he put a ring of pine cones around the entrance. As each one left, it evidently memorized the new surroundings, because when he moved the circle of pine-cones to one side, returning wasps looked for the burrow in the centre of the circle. If cats were as unsophisticated as wasps, they would presumably be thrown into confusion every time we moved our furniture around. Yet a cat returning to a reorganized room is rarely more than curious, even though the room must look and even smell different, if the room has been spring-cleaned as well!

In the middle of our rooms, we tend to have furniture that we can see over the top of, but the same room must look very different from a cat's eye view. Once our imaginary cat has jumped off its windowsill, it may not be able to see the doorway on the far side of the room. So how does it know in which direction to set off, particularly if one or two items of furniture have been moved since it last crossed the room? This may seem a rather trivial problem, since wherever it goes it will eventually get to the doorway, but for a cat foraging over a range of a square kilometre or more, such decisions can be crucial. Cats can build up something like a mental map of their surroundings, although they take rather longer than most people would. Cats can use their maps even if part of the topography changes; presumably they rely on those cues that have not changed to reconstruct the "map". If the opportunity for a short-cut presents itself, they are good at judging whether the new route is shorter. Weighing up a choice between two routes that appear to be of roughly equivalent length, they will usually pick the one that starts off in the direction closest to that of the final goal. To be a successful hunter when game is scarce, the ability not to get lost must be crucial. Therefore, some of the cat's orientation abilities may yet lie undiscovered.

CHAPTER 4

Hunting and Feeding

*T*here are still many cats that earn their keep by their prowess as hunters. Although these are most common in the countryside, it is not unheard of for city-dwellers to keep a cat for the primary purpose of controlling pests around their houses or business premises. Other urban cats, leading a shadowy existence on the fringes of society, must presumably supplement the fruits of scavenging with living prey. However, there is a general trend towards denying the cat its origins as a highly-tuned predator, and replacing this with a more sentimental image. It cannot be denied that there is something faintly disturbing about the abrupt change that comes over many a cat's character as soon as it is through its cat-flap: indoors, the doting dependent; outdoors, as savage a beast as ever stalked the plains of the Serengeti. On a more practical note, the damage that cats do to wildlife can occasionally be devastating in its effects.

Although the cat that brings home the occasional mouse or young bird may worry its owner, very few long-term effects on urban or rural wildlife seem to result. Pet cats are unlikely to have refined their hunting techniques to the limit, and usually catch weak or sickly animals that would soon have succumbed to

When stalking, every sense is
focussed on the prey.

disease or another predator anyway. Although scare stories have appeared based on the sheer numbers of small mammals and birds that cats catch, high mortality rates are a way of life for many of these species. In the United Kingdom, the role of arch-villain has recently passed to the magpie, which has increased in numbers and also preys on young animals. Yet in this case also, long-term damage to the populations of prey species has shown to be fairly unimportant, however distressing the sight of a song-bird's nest after a raid by magpies.

There is no doubt, however, that cats can have a devastating effect when they are introduced on to small islands that lie far out in the ocean, where the local animals and birds have never before been threatened by any mammalian predator. Some of these may be very rare species, perhaps only occurring on a handful of islands, and may be wiped out before they have had a chance to adapt to such a dramatic change in their circumstances. Perhaps the most heart-rending example of such an event is the short and unhappy story of the Stephens Island wren. Every single one of the specimens that we have of this now extinct bird was caught and killed in 1894 by the lighthouse keeper's cat on this island off the coast of New Zealand. Of other species, flightless birds such as penguins are particularly vulnerable. So are birds like petrels, noddies and terns, that rely on islands either to nest on the bare ground, or in holes that are unfortunately large enough to allow the entry of a marauding cat.

FAVOURITE PREY

Popular myth labels the cat as a bird-hunter, but while the occasional cat may become a bird specialist, this idea has probably arisen because birds are usually killed during the day, and their corpses are therefore more evident, whereas mammals are normally hunted at night. It is now firmly established that, where they are available, cats prefer to prey on small mammals, and voles in particular; in North America, ground squirrels and chipmunks are also favourites. More seasonal prey includes young rabbits and hares; the adults of both these species make formidable adversaries, and pose a risk of injury to all but the largest or most skilful of cats. When alternative prey is scarce, for example in hard winters, cats may have to overcome their fear of rabbits.

In parts of Australia and New Zealand, where imported rabbits have become serious pests of agriculture, free-living cats (also imported) can help to keep down their populations. Where summers are warmer than in Britain, cats can eat quite large numbers of insects, although because these tend to be small and rather indigestible, they rarely make a major contribution to the cat's nutrition. In the tropics, cats eat reptiles. Fish, on the other hand, seems to have been introduced by people into the diet of the domestic cat; the fascinating Indian Fishing Cat *Felis viverrina* is a closely related but quite distinct species.

Notable omissions from this "Good Prey Guide" are shrews, rats and mice. Cats often kill these; in fact their reputation as pest controllers often hangs on their readiness to dispatch the latter. However, cats that are not especially hungry rarely eat any of them, especially shrews, which must taste particularly dreadful. Rat meat is way down the list of preferred taste for most cats – less attractive than even the cheapest of supermarket pet foods. Why cats bother to kill unpalatable prey, particularly when they are not even hungry, will be discussed later on; first we must examine the way in which cats hunt.

HUNTING METHODS

Although cats have their individual preferences, they tend to select from within these on the simple basis of what happens to be available. Their highly sensitive vision suggests that they should hunt by moonlight and at dawn and dusk, and lie-up during the day when other predators, better suited to the daylight, have an advantage, but they will usually adapt the timing of their sorties to match the activity of the prey available. Extremes of temperature are avoided, so that during a hot summer cats will hunt mainly at night, while during winter daylight hunting is common. This may, of course, have as much to do with changes in the activity of the prey, as it is to do with the comfort of the cat. House cats that hunt tend to do so when their owners are out, but much of this cannot be classified as serious food-gathering.

The hunting strategy preferred by most cats is to sit and wait in places where prey is usually found. This is an efficient method for small mammals, which often use semi-permanent runways through ground vegetation. It is a virtually useless

(Opposite) Cats that are
brave enough to hunt rats are
still wary of them, even after
they have been killed.

strategy for catching birds. Since the cat cannot conceal itself from detection from above, most birds have little difficulty in avoiding landing near a cat. Bird-hunting cats therefore have to stalk their prey, starting from thick cover. House cats rarely make much of a success of this, and it is hard to avoid the impression that an experienced bird has the measure of the cat long before it flies away, leaving the frustrated predator helplessly rooted to the ground.

Most cats that are allowed outside hunt at least occasionally. Some of them may not do this until they are out of sight of the house, possibly because they have learned that the sight of abandoned corpses provokes a bad reaction in their owner! Various surveys of the diet of outdoor cats have been carried out, sometimes by looking for the remains of bone and fur in cat faeces, sometimes by the examination of the stomach contents of road casualties. It is estimated that between two-fifths and two-thirds of house cats regularly consume prey; animals that are killed but not eaten will of course go undetected unless recorded in some other way. Feral cats are more likely than house cats to take large prey such as rabbits. Since hunting is more of a hobby than a way of life to a house cat, the risk of injury from a rabbit's defensive kick is probably not worthwhile.

Most of the time, cats seem to be fairly lazy and inefficient predators. Their true abilities only emerge in queens that are feeding kittens. Not only does a queen have several new mouths to feed, but every second that she is away from her young leaves them exposed to cold, disease and predation, and maybe even the risk of being killed by a marauding tom cat. The pace of her hunting shifts instantly into overdrive. Dennis Turner and Othmar Meister, who measured this in cats hunting through farmland in Switzerland, found that mother cats caught one item of prey every one-and-a-half hours, while other cats only caught prey a couple of times a day. Hunting trips lasted for about the same time in both groups, but the mothers travelled twice as fast as the other cats, and investigated twice as many hunting sites. They also caught something every three or four pounces, compared to a normal rate of one in twelve or worse. Mothers consume some prey as soon as they catch it, but their altered hormone balance stimulates them to bring most of their catch back to their nest. Many house cats, including entire

(unneutered) and neutered toms, bring newly-caught prey back to their owner's house. Whether this unwelcome habit is linked in any way to the behaviour of mother cats that has just been described is something of a mystery.

THE SERIOUS PREDATOR

Although cats are probably perpetually on the look-out for opportunities for predation, serious hunting brings on a dramatic change in behaviour. Once prey has been spotted, the cat will go into a crouching posture and slink rapidly towards it, keeping close to the ground and making use of cover wherever possible. Once close to striking distance, the cat will often slow down its forward progress, "freezing" with its front paws under its shoulders if it thinks the other animal is looking in its direction, and creeping along the ground when its back is turned. By now, the cat's head is stretched out and its ears are erect and pointing forwards, as if straining for any slight sound that will give a clue as to the prey's next move. The final approach to the prey is usually a brief sprint. In long grass, or when catching insects, a leaping pounce may be used, but wherever possible the cat likes to have its hind legs on the ground as it strikes the prey. If the prey moves just as the final spring is launched, a correction may have to be made, and the result, perhaps with only one of the cat's hind legs on the ground to give stability, may be clumsy enough to permit an escape. As the cat's muzzle approaches the victim, the whiskers are extended forward, and become part of the bite-directing equipment, as described in the previous chapter.

The cat's preferred method of killing is to dislocate the neck of its prey by plunging its canine teeth between the vertebrae. If successful, this will dispatch the prey almost instantaneously. The teeth are probably guided on their murderous way by touch receptors attached to their roots. This may not be effective on large or troublesome animals, like rats or rabbits, and the cat may have to resort to raking the body of its prey with its powerful hind-claws, while searching for a better bite.

Two aspects of hunting behaviour have puzzled biologists for years, and so far there are no convincing explanations for either of them. The first occurs while the cat is waiting to spring.

It will move its hindpaws backwards slightly to improve its reach, and then alternately raise and lower its hind feet. The tip of the tail may also twitch at this point, seemingly uncontrollable. Both of these actions look as if they would give the game away, allowing the prey to escape, and they should therefore have been eliminated during the course of evolution. There have been several explanations for these apparently unnecessary movements. Psychologists have suggested that the cat is venting its frustration at having to wait before it strikes, but it seems unlikely that cats should be so weak-willed at this critical moment, when they can be so inscrutable at other times. It may be that we have a different view of the cat to the one it is presenting to the prey. From the target's point of view, the rear end of the cat may be largely screened by its front end, and so may be moved surreptitiously. I have no explanation myself for the tail-twitching, but the rocking of the hind-paws reminds me of nothing so much as the bouncing gait of a prize-fighter in the ring. Just as he keeps his legs warmed up and ready to take him on to the offensive, so the cat may be keeping its leg muscles set up for the spring. In other words, this may be the way that the cat staves off cramp.

The other mystery is the extraordinary teeth-chattering sound that some cats suddenly produce when they spot an unattainable but tempting prey, such as a bird out of reach in a tree. This noise seems to be specific to this situation, and is never produced on any other occasion. Animals usually vent their frustration by doing something from their normal repertoire but in totally the wrong context. For example, a cat may suddenly start to groom in the middle of a quarrel with another cat. These actions are known as displacement activities, but while we may reasonably suggest that a cat is frustrated when prey is so near yet so far away, the unique nature of the teeth-chattering means that it cannot be a true displacement activity, although this has been suggested. If it is an attempt to lure the bird down to investigate (a sort of opposite to "curiosity killed the cat"), then this has never been reported as being effective.

HOW CATS EAT THEIR PREY
This section should not be read by the squeamish!

Although most pet cats probably eat rather little of what

they may catch, many feral and free-ranging cats need all the nourishment they can get, and become adept at turning their captures into a meal. After the kill, the prey is often carried into cover, presumably to minimize the risk that it will be stolen by a larger cat or another predator. Although it would probably be more efficient if the prey was grasped somewhere in the middle, it is usually dragged rather clumsily along by the scruff of its neck. One explanation given for this is that the cat is still fixated by its quarry's neck, the site of the killing bite, and ignores any other possibilities. As a result, the prey's hindquarters often become dirty, and on arrival at the eating site the cat may shake the prey clean before settling down to eat. Small mammals are eaten from the head downwards. If the cat is not particularly hungry, the result may be one of the hideously decapitated corpses that turn up on doorsteps. If the skull is too strong, the meal will start at the neck, but either way it will usually progress down the body in the direction of the pile of the fur. The skin is often removed by being grasped in the cat's teeth and then tugged and shaken. Birds demand a different technique, to remove the feathers; house cats may lack this skill, or simply not be sufficiently hungry to warrant using it, accounting for the seemingly untouched birds with broken necks that appear in gardens on winter mornings. The feathers are pulled out in the teeth and then spat away, but the rough papillae on the tongue, otherwise used for grooming, now become a liability since scraps of feather become trapped in them. While plucking a bird, a cat can be seen to groom its flanks periodically; rather than to clean the fur, this is done to dislodge the debris from the tongue. The whole business looks very cumbersome, suggesting that a cat that actually eats a bird must indeed be hungry.

THE ROLE OF THE SENSES IN HUNTING

The cat's vision, hearing and sense of smell, not to mention its mobile whiskers, are all primarily adapted for efficiency in hunting. However, they are not used equally at all stages. The places where prey might be hiding are generally found by looking, although the fresh scent of a mouse may sustain a cat's interest in a particular location. Certainly, most cat owners must have noted their pet's fascination with nooks and crannies around the

(Opposite) Not all pounces are as athletic as this one.

garden. The initial detection of the prey is most likely to occur because of some tiny sound that the cat's super-sensitive ears pick up; most cats show an inborn interest in almost any sudden high-pitched sound, like a rustle, scrape or squeak. The ultra-sonic call of a rodent is a particularly effective sound, and with practice cats can distinguish between those made by different species, say voles compared to mice.

Once the cat has worked out the source of the sound, its attention switches to vision, and in particular any sudden movement made by the quarry. Inexperienced cats can completely overlook an animal that does not move, so the habit that many small mammals have of "freezing" as soon as they detect a predator is presumably geared up to this possibility. Vision is the main sense used during the stalk, right up to the moment of the strike. Because cats are long-sighted, the whiskers and the sensitive areas of skin around the mouth then take over to guide the killing bite (*see Chapter 3*). The small sensory hairs around the mouth are important for guiding the skinning or plucking of the prey prior to eating.

More details of the cat's senses can be found in Chapter 2.

HOW KITTENS LEARN TO HUNT

Mouse-hunting mothers are avid teachers of their young, since they have to ensure that their offspring can fend for themselves as quickly as possible. Litters born in hedgerows to feral queens must of necessity be weaned on to prey that has been caught for them, and as they grow their mother will continually challenge them by providing less and less help with obtaining solid food. To begin with, the prey will be partly dismembered, but soon it will simply be left in the nest for the kittens to deal with. Later on it will be brought back still half-alive. This may seem very cruel to us, but to the mother cat it is simply the most essential part of her kittens' education, providing a skill without which they would soon perish. The kittens' predatory behaviour patterns will have already begun to emerge in their play, both with their littermates and with objects, and by providing moving but accessible prey the mother can focus these on a realistic target, and at the same time allow the kittens to associate prey with the satisfaction of hunger. From time to time, if the kittens are reluctant to attack whatever she has brought back, she may attack it herself in front of them, as if to demonstrate the way in which it should be done. There is no evidence to suggest that this is deliberate on the mother's part; it could be an automatic response to the movement and appearance of the prey, that would have happened whether the kittens had been there or not. However, it has been proved that kittens can learn something very quickly if they have first seen their mother do it (*see Chapter 5*).

The mother's role as trainer extends to the sort of prey that the young cats will take. The best technique for catching small prey, such as mice, is learned rapidly and easily, but experience has a much greater effect on whether a kitten will grow up to be an effective predator of larger prey, such as rats. Inexperienced cats are likely to be frightened of these, but they can overcome their fear either by direct encounters with rats, or by observing another cat killing them. Even this is only likely to work if the cat has an outgoing disposition. A combination of the right temperament and experience is presumably required to produce the "good ratter" beloved of farmers. Why some cats end up as bird-hunters, and others do not, is still a mystery.

WHY DO PET CATS HUNT AT ALL?

Many owners are unable to understand why their cat will polish off a meal of some expensive and apparently delectable cat food, only to vanish through the cat flap and reappear half an hour later dragging a helpless or very dead mouse. The answer is that the cat's ancestors, needing to catch several items of prey each day, could not afford the time to wait until one meal had been digested before going in search of the next. This is a direct contrast to the cat's giant cousin the lion, or its distant relative the wolf, which by hunting co-operatively can bring down several days' worth of food at a time and can therefore afford to rest between hunts.

In the domestic cat, hunting and hunger are controlled by quite distinct, though interconnected, parts of the brain. Robert Adamec, a scientist working in Toronto, showed that cats can switch from feeding to hunting and back again at the drop of a metaphorical hat. He allowed experienced ratters to start a meal of cat food, and then arranged for a live rat to run past the bowl. Virtually without exception, his cats broke off from eating, caught the rat, dispatched it, dragged it back to beside the food bowl, and then carried on eating the cat food as if nothing had happened. By comparing their preference for the cat food over fresh rat meat, he was able to establish that his cats did not find rat tasty. However, he also found that if the cat food was replaced by fresh salmon, the cats hesitated before attacking the rat, some to the extent that they finished the whole meal first. Even cats with little experience of hunting will start to hunt prey even if they are not hungry, but hunger does seem to affect whether the hunt is pursued right to the kill. The decision to eat a quarry once it is caught is presumably based on a combination of how ravenous the cat is, and how tasty it expects the prey to be.

Farmers who keep cats primarily as controllers of vermin tend to keep them hungry, on the grounds that this produces a lean, mean exterminator. Certainly, cats that are not fed at all by people can hunt for at least twelve hours out of twenty-four, while well-fed pets may only hunt for two or three. In general, hunger seems to affect the likelihood that a cat will start to hunt, and also whether it will kill, but almost any cat will react to the appearance of prey by starting the predatory sequence.

WHY DO CATS PLAY WITH THEIR PREY?

People who like to run down cat-keeping will often point to the cat's apparently sadistic habit of playing with its prey, not only when it is already weakened by an initial attack, but especially when it is dead. In the cat's defence, what looks like play is really little pieces of real predatory behaviour, but acted out in a disorganized way so that none are particularly effective. Ethologists now think that this means that the cat is trying to obey two conflicting instincts at the same time, one to catch and kill the prey, and the other to keep out of its way to avoid injury. The result is that any attempt to attack the prey is quickly inhibited by a desire to escape; as the cat withdraws so the urge to attack grows stronger, and so on. The result looks, to our eyes, pointless and therefore the cat seems to be playing. Even after the prey is actually dead, some fear seems to persist, and therefore the apparent game may continue for a while. The evidence for this interpretation comes from two observations by Maxeen

Biben at the University of North Carolina, who studied cats preying on mice and rats of various sizes. She noticed that the disruption of normal predation into "play" occurred when her cats were hungry when they encountered rats, animals of which they were evidently wary. It also occurred for smaller prey when the cats had just been fed. In both the situations where "play" occurred, the balance between fear and the need to kill was about equal, even though their actual strengths were very different (both high in the first case, both low in the second). Perhaps our initial judgement of the cat as a cruel tormentor should be replaced by an acceptance that this is the outward sign of a "scaredy-cat"!

NUTRITION

Although the hunting instinct is there under the skin in every cat, the actual amount of hunting that each cat does largely depends on the kind of life it has led, starting in kittenhood and ending with when it had its last meal. No such flexibility exists when we consider the primary purpose of hunting, which is to provide the cat with all the nutrients that it needs. All of the members of the cat family, from the smallest to the lion or tiger, are highly specialized carnivores, in a way that many of their close relatives are not. For example, although most people feed their dogs on meat, dogs and their cousins the wolves and coyotes are really omnivores, capable of living on a largely vegetarian diet if necessary, although they prefer meat if they can get it. Bears, also members of the carnivore group, really do like honey, as well as all sorts of berries, tubers and nuts. The pandas are carnivores that have given up eating meat entirely, and live exclusively on plants.

Since omnivorous animals cannot always control the proportions of plant and animal food in their diet, they generally have the ability to convert nutrients obtained from one of these sources into a form that makes up for the lack of the other source. At some early stage in the evolution of the cat family, many of these abilities were lost. Presumably this happened as a side-effect of the specialization to meat-eating, but since metabolic processes cannot be traced from fossils, the actual course of events will never be known. Since it is much easier to lose a part of metabolism than it is to regain it, the modern cat family is "stuck" with meat-eating. In fact, despite the many advances made recently in our understanding of feline nutrition, it is still impossible to make a vegetarian cat food without including synthetic additives.

An all-meat diet differs in several ways from the mixed diet that most humans are used to. It contains a large proportion of protein and fat, and relatively little carbohydrate. Meat-eating therefore produces an automatic surplus of protein, so the proteins are normally broken down to produce energy, as well as being used for growth and repair of tissues. Omnivores may be short of protein at certain stages in their lives when they are forced to live on low-quality foods, and are able to conserve protein already in the body by switching off the protein-degrading processes in the liver. The cat has only a limited ability to do this; the enzymes responsible can be slowed down but not stopped entirely, with the result that a cat's minimum protein requirement is the highest of any mammal that has been investigated. This is less apparent in kittens, where large amounts of protein are used in growth, but even so they need more (at least 18 per cent of the diet) than puppies do (12 per cent). Adult cats need about as much protein as a growing puppy, in proportion to the amount that each eats, and three times as much as an adult dog (4 per cent). Cats also need unusually large amounts of some of the amino-acids, the building-blocks of proteins, especially those that contain sulphur atoms. These are used in particular for making hair (part of the acrid smell of singed hair is due to the sulphur it contains), so the cat's thick coat can be blamed for some of this requirement.

Another sulphur-containing amino-acid, taurine, which is rarely mentioned in human nutrition, is essential for the cat's health. In most animals taurine is an obscure intermediate in the conversion of another amino-acid, cysteine, into other forms required by the body. Cats have lost the ability to make taurine in this way, and must therefore obtain it from their diet. Insufficient taurine is not damaging short-term, but if the lack is prolonged, it can lead to degeneration of both the retina in the eye and the muscles of the heart.

Cats tend to like fats of many kinds, and can digest oils refined from plants, like sunflower and olive oils, just as readily as lard, butter and other fats from animal sources. There is one major difference, however, between the metabolism of fats by cats and most other mammals: cats require trace amounts of arachidonic acid, which they then convert into prostaglandins, hormone-like materials that are essential for reproduction. Most omnivores can make all the prostaglandins they need from linoleic acid, a common constituent of plant oils, but cats have lost this ability, and without arachidonic acid in her diet a queen cat will not come into season. Arachidonic acid is most abundant in animal tissue, but because it is destroyed by heat it is often absent from extracted fats such as lard. The only available plant-based source of this acid is evening primrose oil, which must therefore be added to vegetarian cat foods.

Sugars and other sweet things mean very little to a cat, because it cannot taste them (*see Chapter 2*). The cat's stomach can cope with carbohydrates reasonably well, which is why most commercial dry cat foods can be based on cereals. There is one sugar that cats find it hard to digest, and that is lactose, found in cow's milk. Undigested lactose passes through to the hind-gut, where it is met by a horde of bacteria ready and waiting to ferment it for their own benefit. The result is often diarrhoea, which is why those proprietary cat milks that are formulated to contain only small amounts of lactose are much more suitable for cats than cow's milk.

Vitamins have become a prominent part of the public consciousness of a healthy lifestyle in the past few years. So do cats need vitamin supplements? In most cases, the answer is no; scientific understanding of the cat's need for vitamins is advanced and the great majority of proprietary petfoods contain just the right amount. Supplementation can indeed be harmful and should only be used where essential. Personally, I have only used vitamin pills once, when my fish-loving cat Lucy was pregnant for the first time, and most of the commercially-available all-fish cat foods were still unsupplemented.

It is worth checking whether a cat food is labelled as the "complete" type, or as "complementary", in which case they may not be. The dangers of incomplete nutrition multiply for a cat fed exclusively on a home-cooked diet, and it is wise to include at least some of the "complete prepared" type to ensure continuing good health.

Farm cats depend on
handouts from humans for
much of their food.

Uncooked fish can lead to vitamin deficiencies, because it contains enzymes that break down thiamine, a vitamin that cats require in abnormally large amounts. Most commercial cat food is supplemented with thiamine. Because this vitamin is destroyed by heat, prolonged cooking of meat or fish can also result in thiamine-deficient food. Niacin and vitamin A are essential for cats, but vitamin C is not. Humans, apes and guinea-pigs are among the few mammals that require vitamin C; dogs and cats can make all they need from their diet. Vitamin A is essential for making the visual pigment, rhodopsin, in the retina of the eye, and for many other functions in the body. Most animals, including dogs, can make rhodopsin from the yellow and orange pigments (carotenes) found in fruits and vegetables; cats cannot, and require a supply of vitamin A, which is particularly abundant in liver. An excessive intake of this vitamin can lead to a crippling bone disease, so it is best to avoid feeding cats on large amounts of liver or fish liver oils.

WHAT DO CATS LIKE TO EAT, AND WHY?

Cats ought to eat what is good for them, and more specifically, to satisfy the nutritional requirements that have just been described. For a carnivore, achieving this should be straightforward. As the food psychologist Paul Rozin once said of another member of the cat family "only vitamin-deficient zebras can produce vitamin-deficient lions". African wildcats, the ancestors of the domestic cat, could probably obtain a balanced diet by adopting the simple rule "only eat things that are furry and run away". Now that the pet food industry has taken over the task of providing for the domestic cat's nutritional needs, a new general rule could be "trust your owner". However, it is only during the past two decades that we have come to understand exactly what the cat needs in its food. During the whole history of the domestic cat it has had to survive on a mixed diet of hunting, scavenging and handouts from man. Cats that were able to pick out the best things to eat have survived, whereas those which could not will have failed to breed, particularly since pregnancy and lactation are the most nutritionally stressful times in a cat's life. Therefore, over the generations, the ability to make the right choices has spread throughout the species, and is still present today. Many farm cats live by scavenging and miscellaneous handouts, and by looking at the choices they face, we can probably work out what abilities accrued during the course of evolution.

A cursory listing of the types of food that farm cats eat – pigswill, carrion, waste food from restaurants – immediately rules out the possibility of framing any simple rules like the two suggested above. Cats can gather quite diverse information about a food before they even start eating it. What does it look like? What does it smell of? Is it in a location that has yielded food in the past, or is this a new source? Are other cats eating it? A single lick can add information about its taste. However, none of these are likely to provide unambiguous information about its nutritional content. Nutrients come in many forms, and nutritionally similar foods can taste and smell very different. This rules out any possibility that cats could instinctively recognize foods rich in protein, for example, other than those that they have killed for themselves. Even vitamins like thiamine, which have reasonably distinctive tastes, do not seem to be detected by the flavour that they give to food.

Given that instinct is unlikely to work, cats must have to learn what is good to eat as they go along. This process starts in kittenhood, in parallel with the development of the hunting skills described earlier in this chapter. Kittens initially eat what they can see their mother eating; it is also likely that they detect the smell of foods on the fur around her mouth. It is even conceivable this process starts before weaning, through faint traces of flavours in their mother's milk of the foods that she has eaten recently. This certainly happens in pigs, because the first solid food given to piglets is much more likely to be accepted if it tastes like their mother's feed. Mother cats that eat unusual foods, such as mashed potato or banana, pass these preferences on to their kittens.

Equipped with some instinctive knowledge of foods, and some more information obtained at their mother's knee, so to speak, young cats continue broadening their experience as they encounter new foods. Perhaps the most important thing to learn is which foods to avoid; this not only includes foods that are actually poisonous, but also those that are so nutritionally unbalanced that they can be eaten only occasionally, or even not at all. One example of the latter are foods which contain none of the amino-acid arginine. Cats, unlike most other mammals, require arginine in order to be able to excrete urea, and a protein-rich meal containing little or no arginine leads immediately to a build-up of ammonia in the blood. This usually causes vomiting, and the cat becomes lethargic. Foods that lack thiamine, a vitamin used in digestion itself, rapidly lead to anorexia, and the cat can only be tempted to eat again by something that is not only tasty, but also quite distinct in flavour from the deficient food.

The process that enables cats to avoid foods that make them ill is known as "taste aversion learning". Although it has not been studied to any extent in cats, the basic mechanisms are known in detail from studies of rats. These are particularly interesting to animal psychologists because taste aversion breaks one of the cardinal rules of associative learning (*as described in Chapter 2*) that the stimulus (the taste) and the response (the sickness) should occur very close together in time for learning to be efficient. Not only is there often a delay of many minutes or even hours between eating a food and any unpleasant consequences, but it often only takes one such occurrence to put the animal off that food for weeks or even months.

Taste aversion learning is, as its name implies, specific to tastes; the appearance of the food, or the place where it is eaten, are not learned. In this way the chances of the wrong association being made are minimized; for example, cats do not avoid places where they are taken ill, but at that moment they do recall the flavour of the food that they ate last, and associate that with the illness. Mistakes can happen, however, and such is the power of this type of learning that these errors are not confined to animals. Have you ever tried a new dish just at the moment you came down with a virus? It is a common experience that you will, irrationally, avoid that food for some considerable time afterwards. Cats can probably make similar mistakes, which might account for some otherwise inexplicable refusals of previously palatable foods.

WHY DON'T CATS GET FAT?

While dogs generally finish up everything they are offered, cats are renowned for being "finicky eaters". Most of them seem to be able to manage their weight very well, although about 10 per cent over-eat if their owners allow them. Such accurate control implies that cats are very good counters of calories, but some of the scientific evidence has suggested that cats do not increase their intake as the number of calories in their food is reduced. However, the "high-bulk" foods that were used in these trials used clay or cellulose to provide the bulk, and most cats dislike the taste of both these substances intensely. The fact that they under-ate when offered such diets is more of a testimony to their discerning palates than an indication that they cannot judge the calorific value of their food. Other trials, in which dry foods were compared with canned, or plain water was used as the diluting agent, have confirmed what the cat's sleek physique had told us all along, that their appetite adjusts to take account of how much they have eaten at previous meals. Very concentrated foods, containing a high proportion of fat, are eaten sparingly, so that again the cat's weight changes very little or not at all.

This difference between dogs and cats is no accident; it stems from the feeding habits of their ancestors, the wolf and the wildcat. Wolves often hunt in packs, and in that way can tackle moose, caribou and elk, prey that is much larger than they are. After the kill, there is tremendous competition between members of the pack to eat as much as possible of the carcase. Wolves will therefore gorge themselves if given the opportunity, and then sleep and rest until they need to hunt again. Domestic dogs have lost the urge to hunt, but, in many breeds, not the urge to gorge. The presence of another dog will often lead to frenzied eating, another behavioural trait inherited from the wolf. Cats, being solitary hunters of small prey, have to adopt a quite different strategy. Having no opportunity to gorge, and needing to kill at least once each day, they have evolved mechanisms to keep their weight on the lean side, always fit and trim for hunting. The provision of food by humans, which has effectively lifted this restriction, seems in practice to have had little effect.

Cats are, however, very flexible in the number of times a day that they need to eat. Two meals is the usually accepted minimum, but cats allowed to eat whenever they want will take between twelve and twenty small meals a day, spread throughout the twenty-four hours, but slightly larger in daylight hours than at night. There is no evidence that such a regime is any better than fewer, larger meals; it is simply what cats do if left entirely to their own devices. It does mean that there is nothing wrong if you leave some dry cat food available all the time. Unlike many humans, most cats can regulate what they eat between meals, and so never get fat! Main meals can be offered two or three times each day. Cats will quickly learn the signs that show that meal-times are approaching, and in this way can be trained to eat at particular times. Other cats, one of my own included, train their owners to feed them to *their* schedule!

<u>WHY DO SOME CATS EAT ONLY ONE KIND OF FOOD?</u>

My mother cat Lucy is the archetypal fish-loving cat. Despite popular myth, many cats prefer meat to fish, but a few, like Lucy, will eat nothing else. I have heard of other cats that will only eat one brand of commercial pet food. Such cats steadfastly refuse to eat foods that most cats find very acceptable. The reasons may vary from individual to individual (Lucy seems never to have educated her palate far beyond the sardines that she was first weaned on to), but in many cases the cat may simply be afraid of things that are new to them. This is a protective mechanism, which acts as a first line of defence against all kinds of potentially dangerous experiences, and which affects some individuals more than others. When first offered a new food, some cats simply spend a little longer than usual sniffing it before they eat. Others will eat only a little at the first time of offering, although they may later develop a preference for that food. The most nervous or sensitive cats may simply refuse to eat any new food at all. Complete refusal to eat is more likely if several new experiences occur together, such as feeding a new food in a different bowl to the usual, or in a different room. Additions to the diet should therefore be introduced carefully, as part of the usual routine, and when the cat is relaxed. However, neophobia is not the only reason why hungry cats refuse to eat; they may simply not like what they have been offered! Cats are generally much "fussier" about their food than any other domesticated animal. They also seem to be able to educate their palates, so that a few servings of a very tasty food can lead to a subsequent rejection of a food which they previously accepted.

DO CATS LIKE A CHANGE OF DIET?

Provided neophobia is not a problem, cats relish contrasts of taste. The great variety of commercial cat foods that are available nowadays is not, as was once put to me on the "Today" programme, only there to give indulgent cat owners a choice. Many cats get bored if they are offered the same variety of the same brand of food day after day. My spoiled long-haired male cat Splodge cannot bear more than one small meal of any particular food each day, with the result that one corner of our fridge always contains three open cans of cat food. Such demands would seem out of place in the competitive world of the farmyard, yet when David Macdonald, of Oxford University, and I surveyed three farms, we found that at each farm most of the cats preferred foods that were common at the other two farms, but rare at their own. Thus the need for variety is probably common to all cats, whatever their lifestyle. There is no nutritional need for a pet cat to demand a change of diet, when almost every food contains all the nutrition it could require. Farm cats, on the other hand, probably need some way of avoiding eating too much of any one food, in case it turns out to be mildly toxic or, more likely, nutritionally inadequate. Before the advent of modern, balanced pet foods, this would be a useful strategy for any cat to adopt, and it evidently still persists today.

CHAPTER 5

Growing Up

Kittens are cute, of course, but they do not stay kittens for long. Compared to a human infant, they mature at a staggering rate. If our own children grew up as quickly, they would be earning a living by the time they were three years old. There is a simple reason for this rapid development: in the wild, cat mothers cannot go on catching enough food for the whole litter for very long, and the process of evolution has ensured that this has become part of the cat's nature.

If a female cat is to pass her genes on to the next generation, and the one after that, she must produce some kittens that survive long enough to produce kittens of their own. If she fails in this, all her genes are lost, for ever. The vast majority of those genes will be identical to genes carried by other cats, but gradually, often over the course of hundreds or even thousands of generations of cats, genes which lead to unsuccessful breeding will disappear. Their places will be taken by genes that promote the production of viable young.

Many genes produce visible or invisible changes in the body itself; those producing the different coat colours, and the lack of binocular vision in some Siamese cats, have already been discussed. Other genes, still poorly understood, affect the way that cats behave; for example, some influence the way that a mother cat behaves towards her kittens. A female cat that inherits a good set of "motherhood genes" from her parents is likely to produce several offspring that survive to adulthood, that will in

(Opposite) In a large litter, kittens compete for the teats that produce the most milk.

turn pass some of those genes on to their own kittens. Conversely, a mother that has some deficiency in her "motherhood genes" is unlikely to be successful at producing kittens, so those genes tend to die out. For example, some female cats seem to have great difficulty in distinguishing between their newborn kittens and the placentas, and attempt to eat both. If this was an inherited tendency, it is easy to see why it would die out in just a few generations, were it not for the intervention of a human "midwife". Poor mothers produce few kittens, and eventually their family line disappears.

However, a queen cat can produce one or two litters each year for several years, even in the wild. Her genes will survive provided that any one of those litters lives, but she has no idea which are the kittens that are going to survive to breed in their turn. If she had, she could put all her effort into giving them the best start possible, even if it exhausted her to the point that she could no longer produce any more kittens. But she does not have this knowledge, so she must constantly be balancing her options: whether to allow her current kittens to remain dependent for a little longer, or whether to put her own interests first and get back into peak condition before mating again and producing the next litter.

The kittens have no such compromises to make. Each one wants the best possible start in life for itself. Its littermates only share half its genes (assuming that the mother only mated with one tom) and its brothers and sisters in other litters may only share a quarter (assuming that their mother's other litters were sired by a different tom). Therefore at some point in the development of any litter there comes a time when the mother and the kittens are in conflict: the kittens want to keep the free meals going as long as possible, while the mother wants them off her hands so that she can be fit and ready to produce her next brood.

All this has been explained as if the mothers and the kittens were making conscious decisions. Of course, they are not. The "decisions" are made for them through their genes, and they are quite oblivious of the evolutionary events that shaped them. But the fact remains that, if no human assistance is available, any strategy that deviates far from this balance between the needs of the mother and the needs of the kitten will not persist. A mother that abandons each litter when it is too young to fend for itself will have many kittens in her lifetime but no descendants, because none will survive to adulthood. A mother that gives her all to her first litter, and perishes in the attempt, runs the risk that they will be wiped out by some catastrophe, such as an outbreak of disease. In any case, the amount that she can give them will be limited by the extent to which she stays strong enough to continue hunting.

The net result of all this conflict is that kittens, in common with many young mammals, mature very quickly. The process is so fascinating that it is worth most of a chapter. First of all, however, we will concentrate on the mother, for she creates the environment in which the kittens start their lives.

MOTHER CATS

I shall never forget the amazement with which I watched my female cat Lucy, then just one year old, dealing with her newborn kittens as if it was something she had done a thousand times. It was natural to think that her seemingly effortless skill was the expression of deep-rooted maternal instincts, although these might also have been influenced by the experience of watching her own mother. Instinct is often betrayed by its imperfections, and to begin with Lucy seemed to have little idea of what her kittens looked or even smelled like. She was, however, immediately responsive to the slightest noise that they made, rushing back to the nest if one cried while she was snatching a few moments to eat, getting up and curling round in a new position if one had ended up behind her, rolling on to her back to expose all six teats if two kittens were scrapping over where to feed. As her first kittens grew up, she began to recognize them by their appearance as well as their voices, and it has been obvious that she has understood much more about what kittens are when she has had her subsequent litters. It is perhaps surprising to us, who have a clear idea what babies are like whether or not we have had one of our own, that the cat's mind can produce such successful maternal care at its first attempt without following some conscious model of what it is supposed to be doing. Nevertheless, that seems to be the case, and we can only marvel at the effortless way it is carried off. For those who have never had that pleasure, a description of the events follows.

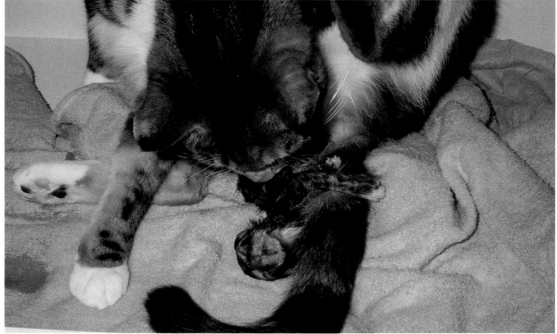

For several weeks prior to the birth the mother-to-be will devote much of her time to seeking out suitable nest-sites. In the wild, the correct choice of site may make the difference between life and death for her kittens. Gillian Kerby, in her study of Oxfordshire farm cats, found that females that chose nest-sites that were exposed and a long way from the farm left no surviving descendants. Farm kittens have many potential enemies, including predatory birds, dogs and even tom cats, but in damp climates the main dangers are from exposure to rain and illness. It is common for whole litters to be wiped out within a few days by an outbreak of 'flu or enteritis. A pet cat should have no such fears, but instinct makes sure that she is just as diligent as any farm cat in inspecting every cupboard, nook and cranny in the house before deciding on one in which to give birth. Since her basic requirements are warmth, peace, quiet, shelter and shadows, it is quite easy for her owners to provide a site that suits the rest of the household, rather than the airing cupboard, which probably does not. Lucy was easily persuaded to use an empty drawer lined with old towels, placed next to a radiator and

(Opposite) Lucy, the author's cat, delivers a kitten. It is born still encased in its shiny sac, which she quickly rasps off with her tongue so that the kitten can take its first breath.
(Below, this page) While they are still in the nest, kittens urinate and defaecate only while being groomed by their mothers (see page 121).

roofed over with a spare shelf supported on boxes. Another towel half-covering the open front of this nest made the interior darker and seemingly even more attractive. It is worthwhile building two such nests, not only to give the queen a choice, but also to provide her with somewhere to move her kittens later on, if that is what she decides to do.

During the hours leading up to the birth, the queen cleans herself thoroughly, particularly around her teats and at the opening of the birth canal. Some queens are very restless in the last hour or so, others are not. As each kitten is born, she rasps away the remains of the sac in which it has spent its first two months. Sometimes the kitten is born completely enclosed in this sac, and if the queen seems to be having difficulty in removing it, a little human help with the corner of a towel may be welcome. Soon after the arrival of each kitten, its placenta is delivered, and this is promptly eaten by the queen. This is not a sight for the squeamish, but it provides essential nourishment for a wild queen, who will have little opportunity for hunting over the next few days. She also licks the kitten thoroughly, apparently stimulated to do so by the smell of her own amniotic fluid. This ensures that the kitten's fur dries quickly, reducing the risk that it will become chilled. It also means that there is very little mess left after kittening, saving the owners a chore! Occasionally and tragically, the mother's instincts malfunction, perhaps because of stress, and she attempts to eat the newborn kittens as well. It may be possible to distract her attention at this stage, giving her the chance to recognize the kittens for what they are, but sadly some felines never seem to grasp the art of motherhood.

Birth may take anything up to twenty-four hours if the litter is a large one. Even in a litter of two, the first kitten will probably be suckling greedily before the second one is born. For the first day and night, the mother scarcely leaves her litter, lying in a curve around them to make it easy for them to find her teats, and also to keep them warm, for at this stage the kittens are unable to maintain their own body temperature. Her devotion scarcely wanes over the next three or four weeks, when she will spend, on average, over sixteen hours in the nest each day. During that time she is totally responsible for the kittens' care; not only does she feed them, but she grooms them regularly. Few people I have asked realize, until it is pointed out to them, that the nest is

becomes contaminated with excreta and the remains of half-finished meals, but the mother cat is so fastidious that this is unlikely to apply in this instance. She may move them if she sees an unfamiliar or hostile cat or dog nearby; nests can be conspicuous if full of hungry, crying kittens, and the mother may feel that she should move them to somewhere more secure. Hilary Feldman, of Cambridge University, has recently made a study of the nest-moving habits of cats living outdoors, the conditions under which the habits presumably evolved. She was able to confirm that nest sanitation was an unlikely explanation. Sites vacated by one family were often quickly re-occupied by another, with no apparent ill-effects. Families consisting of one mother and her offspring rarely moved sites until the kittens were old enough to complete at least part of the journey under their own steam. With only one adult to do all the carrying, kittens will have to be left unprotected at both the old and the new nest-site until the move is complete, and this risk may inhibit the mother. Dr Feldman found that early nest-moving was much more common in litters which were being cared for by more than one adult, perhaps because the kittens can be much better protected (communal breeding is described in much more detail in Chapter 7). As weaning approaches, most moves are in the general direction of the main feeding areas. Dr Gillian Kerby's studies at Oxford University have shown that weaning is a critical time for farm kittens, and if they have to travel long distances to feed, they may eventually perish. Of course, this sort of explanation is unlikely to apply indoors, where the whole family can be fed close to the nest.

THE KITTEN'S WORLD

When it is newborn, the kitten's perception of the world must be very limited, although presumably quite adequate, since its mother takes total charge of it at this stage. As we have seen, kittens are born with a sense of touch, the ability to tell down from up, and a rudimentary sense of smell. Smell is probably used all the time during the first few weeks, particularly once the kitten is strong enough to venture outside the nest. Taste probably matures over the same period as olfaction, but the vomeronasal organ, the second sense of smell described in

(Opposite) A kitten pauses as it reaches an apparently sheer drop. In fact, the kitten is walking on a sheet of glass that extends well beyond the edge, which is underneath the glass. The chequered pattern is there to make the edge look obvious, and the whole setup is known as a visual cliff apparatus, used to measure the development of 3-D vision. Younger kittens walk straight out across the glass, appearing not to notice the edge.

Chapter 2, is not used until the kitten is five to seven weeks old, when the "gape" response is first seen. Neither sight nor hearing are much use for the first few days, since both ears and eyes are sealed up. Vision and hearing develop in parallel over the next five weeks.

A newborn kitten's ear canals are blocked in several places by folds of skin, but these gradually pull apart. At the same time, the external ear or pinna unfolds, like a flower appearing from a bud. The inside of the outer ear becomes corrugated, providing the subtle differences between sounds coming from different directions that will soon enable the kitten to pinpoint the source of anything it hears (*see Chapter 2*). However, the ear-drum itself is probably working even while all these changes are going on, because kittens that are only a few days old will respond to loud noises by starting and lifting up their heads. Recognition of the mother's kitten-call follows the full opening of the ears by just a day or so, and by the early part of the third week of its life, the kitten will turn its head towards her call. A week later, it will know that a cat that growls or yowls means something very different, and that it should run away.

I was once telephoned by an anxious owner whose cat had given birth in a flower-bed. He had managed to move mother and kittens indoors, and while doing so had noticed that their eyes were already beginning to open. He suspected that this precocious development had been brought on by the kitten's early experience of broad daylight, but in fact the tendency came equally from their mother and father. The timing of eye-opening is inherited from both parents, and various tremendously, from within twenty-four hours of birth to over two weeks later. It is unlikely that early opening is much advantage, however. The eyelids peel apart over about a day, revealing eyes which start off looking very cloudy. The optic fluid, through which light must travel to reach the retina, does not clear completely until the kitten is at least four weeks old. Between the second and tenth weeks of life, the amount of detail that the kitten can see increases by more than sixteen times. The kittens quickly learn what their mother looks like, and by the time they are three weeks old they tend to recognize her by her appearance, rather than by her smell. A couple of days later they are able to follow her with their eyes as she moves about.

At this stage, the ability to see in three dimensions is still developing (*see Chapter 2*), and it is not until the end of the first month or the beginning of the second that the world takes on a reliable sense of depth. Scientists have tested this in all sorts of animals, using an apparatus called a visual cliff (*see photograph on page 127*). Perception of depth must be a real bonus, because at this stage the kittens can begin to make connections between their surroundings and what they look like, and can avoid bumping into things as they career around near the nest. However, they still do not seem to realize what their own paws look like! If you gently lower a four-week-old kitten towards the ground, it will extend its front paws just before it touches down. This makes it look as if it knows what it is doing, but in fact the landing is controlled by a reflex. This has been proved by putting kittens on a surface that has gaps or holes in it; at four to five weeks of age, most kittens just stick their paws straight out, whether there is something solid immediately below or not. In another week or so, they have learned to move their paws to miss the gaps, guiding them by direct co-ordination between eye and limb.

TOWARDS INDEPENDENCE

Although to begin with their actions are largely guided by instinct, kittens start to learn almost as soon as they are out of the womb. Even a two-day-old kitten can remember which teats produce the most milk. By the end of their first week, kittens know the smell of their own nest and, if they stray out of it, can use this information to find their way back, although they may still be blind. Later on, once their eyes are open, they learn what their nest looks like as well, but its appearance does not become more important than its smell until they are three or four weeks old.

Once they are about two-and-a-half to three weeks old, kittens begin to show the first signs of independence from their mother. As soon as they are able to walk they should begin to use a litter-tray, although many kittens' first impression of litter is that it is a very crunchy kind of cat food. By this stage they have control over their own urination and defaecation, instead of having to rely on grooming by their mother. Instead of the queen encouraging the kittens to suckle, they begin to try to take charge of their own meal-times. If the mother is a pet, this is the time to start introducing the kittens to solid food; they should have a few teeth by now, which will increase to a full set of milk teeth by about five weeks. For kittens born outdoors to a hunting mother, this is the stage at which she will begin to bring prey into the nest. To begin with, the prey will be cut up for them, but as they get older they will be expected to do more and more for themselves. To encourage them to learn how to hunt, the mother will start to bring prey back half-alive. This seems cruel to our human sensibilities, but it is really just the expression of the mother's instincts, trying to give her kittens their independence as soon as possible.

She may also reduce the amount of time that she is available to nurse her kittens. This is much less noticeable in litters of two or three kittens, which may be allowed to go on suckling until they are two or three months old. Female kittens that stay with their mothers may go on suckling intermittently for years. There are even some recorded instances of daughters nursing their own kittens while suckling from their mothers! Large litters are a different matter, because as they get larger they place a tremendous nutritional burden on their mother, which she may not be able to compensate for even if she is being fed several times a day by her owner. Queens that have to hunt can lose six or more grammes of their body weight each day while they are nursing, and the conflict between her well-being and the kittens', as described at the beginning of this chapter, starts to become acute. Sometime between three and five weeks of age, the kittens will find that the mother is keeping out of their way, or if she is with them, they will find her much less ready to adopt the nursing position. They may actually stop growing at this point. The mother may seem to have become rather heartless, but within a few days she will let them feed from her again. In the meantime, her actions have probably encouraged them to eat more solid food, so from that time on her burden will be reduced.

KITTEN CALLS

Kittens can make a variety of high-pitched cries from when they are only a few hours old, and very young kittens can also make a kind of chuckling sound. The cries vary in intensity, pitch and length, and these variations may convey some meaning, although they are all ultimately aimed at getting the mother's attention. There seem to be three main reasons why kittens cry; cold, isolation, and being trapped. Cold produces high-pitched, rapid squeaks, which are particularly intense when the kittens are young, but reduce as it gets older. This makes sense, because the older the kittens get, the better they are able to cope with cold. A kitten that accidentally gets on the wrong side of its mother, or even underneath her, when she gets back into the nest, will cry repeatedly until she releases it, whatever its age. Separation from the mother induces most crying when the kitten is three to four weeks old. Even when kittens are mobile and perfectly capable of finding their mother for themselves, they may still "try it on" until they are four or five months old.

WATCHING MOTHER

Kittens have to grow up much too quickly to be able to learn everything by trial and error. They instinctively focus on what their mother is doing; as described in the previous chapter, this enables them to pick up rapidly what they should eat, and how to hunt. Psychologists have disagreed over how this kind of learning takes place. It does not seem to be quite as sophisticated as the ways in which people learn skills from one another. For example, when we show someone how to do something, we very often go through the actions required in a kind of slow motion. Demonstrations of this kind seem to be ineffective when training kittens, nor have cats ever been seen to do them (of course, we also back up our actions by verbal instructions, something which an animal, having no language, cannot do). A kitten, having seen an adult cat or another kitten achieve something, will succeed at the same task much more quickly than if it had been allowed to work it out for itself. The simplest explanation is that the kitten's attention becomes focussed on the components of the problem to be solved. A kitten will learn much more quickly if the demonstrator is its mother, or another familiar cat; presumably an unfamiliar cat is a distraction, and the kitten may be so concerned by the potential threat posed by a stranger that it pays little attention to what it is doing.

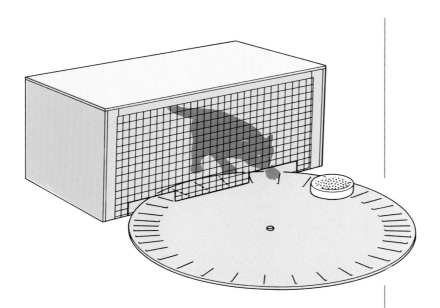

Perhaps surprisingly, watching another cat try and then succeed in solving a problem is a more effective lesson than watching a cat that has perfected what it has to do. This was discovered by Marvin Herbert, working at the University of Nebraska in 1942. In one of his experiments, he placed a bowl containing a small amount of food on a turntable. If the cat turned the turntable in either direction, it would eventually swing round into the box. The turntable was quite difficult to turn, so it would take more than a single erratic swipe of a paw to spin it round. On their first attempts, most of the cats took one or two minutes to get the food, improving to a few seconds after plenty of practice. On the other side of the turntable, two or three cats watched the process, without being allowed to touch the turntable.

In one experiment, one of two six-month-old sisters, Tip and Sis, did the demonstrating while their other sisters Tige and Blackie watched. The very first time that Tige was allowed to turn the turntable, she retrieved the food in 21 seconds; Blackie did even better, in 14 seconds. They had been able to observe the thirty attempts that their sisters made, including the ones at the beginning that took a minute or two of trial and error.

Other kittens, that had been allowed to watch only the last fifteen, near-perfect, performances, took about a minute to retrieve the food. They behaved as if they expected the solution to be easy, and when a few casual flicks of the turntable did not pay off, they "gave up" for a few moments. They had learned that the turntable was relevant to obtaining the food, but had not paid attention to the actions required.

KITTENS PLAYING

As soon as their eyes and ears are open, and they have developed a reasonable amount of co-ordination, but often before they can walk, kittens begin to play the games that are part of their charm. No-one doubts that they are, indeed, playing, but biologists have found play much harder to get to grips with than many other aspects of kitten behaviour. For example, it is quite obvious why a kitten is born with a suckling reflex, and a great deal is known about the kinds of stimuli that trigger it, and how it changes as the kitten grows. Play, on the other hand, is apparently purposeless. It consists of pieces of behaviour, many of which look rather like things that adults do, that are performed for no obvious reason, and often in an incomplete way. For example, kittens often look as if they are going to bite each other, but they rarely hurt each other. Many of the actions that they perform on each other are similar to those used by an adult cat when it is dealing with prey, but they are put together in such a disorganized way that they only superficially resemble predatory behaviour. What is all this activity for? This is a question that has been asked many times, and there are still no satisfactory answers. Play must be important; if the mother produces too little milk to satisfy her growing litter, they will actually spend *more* time playing, despite their hunger. We will return to the possible functions of play, but first its various stages must be described.

To begin with, kittens play at rough-and-tumble in the nest, clumsily rolling one another over and over. Even at this early stage, at about three weeks of age, one characteristic posture is used that will continue to be seen throughout kittenhood. This is known as "Belly-Up", and is remarkably similar to a posture used by an adult cat to deal with large prey, or when defending itself against an attack by another cat. The kitten lies on its back, perhaps holding the other kitten with its front paws, and treading with its hind legs. In the adult version, the hind legs are raked rapidly to and fro with claws extended. The difference between the kitten and adult performances seem to be in the intensity with which they are performed, and the damage they are intended to cause. This is the key difference that distinguishes much of play from "purposeful" behaviour. It is also important that both participants are sure that the other is only playing, and kittens sometimes use an open-mouthed "play-face" to indicate this. This signal is also used by other carnivores, for example young polecats and puppies.

The complementary position to Belly-Up is Stand-Up, and joins the repertoire as soon as the kitten is strong enough to stand on all four paws, and can lunge across a kitten that is lying on its back. Well co-ordinated walking and running adds many new possibilities, including a playful version of pouncing. This, with Belly-Up and Stand-Up, are among the most common patterns used by a kitten to invite another to start playing. As they get older, play can also be started by one kitten standing on its hind legs, with its front paws held out in front (known, prosaically, as Vertical Stance). Even more appealing is the kitten's comical (and, of course, unintended) imitation of a crab; it arches its back, curls its tail around in an arc, and walks sideways. Known as Side-Step, this is sometimes a rather ineffective way to start a game, because the other kitten often simply responds by performing is own Side-Step. This little dance can persist through several repetitions, until one kitten either breaks off or, for example, pounces on the other. Possibly it may indicate the kitten's uncertainty about whether it really wants to play and by the time the litter is twelve weeks old, it is rarely performed. Most other playful actions have counterparts that tend to keep the bout going. For example, if one kitten indicates that it is about to pounce, or stands on its hind legs in a Vertical Stance, the other will usually go Belly-Up, inviting the first to close in to a Stand-Up. After a brief bout of wrestling one will break free; it may either restart the proceedings with one of the postures already mentioned, or attempt to escape, something that often results in a chase. A leap off the ground, with the back arched and the tail curled upwards, Horizontal Leap, is often performed at the end of a bout and may be a signal given by the kitten that wants to stop playing.

For much of their time, up to the completion of weaning at about seven or eight weeks, kittens generally prefer to play with their littermates rather than play objects. It is common practice to home kittens at about eight weeks old, but if some of them stay together they will begin to divide their mutual games into two different types. One looks rather similar to the kind of games that they play on their own, with toys, and consists of

(Left, below) Two young kittens play-fighting – the one on its back is using the "play-face" to indicate its willingness to play.
(Centre) A kitten pounces on an insect.
(Right) A pair of older kittens dance around each other, using the postures termed "side-step" and "vertical stance" (far right).

predatory actions, such as pouncing and biting. The other includes the "dancing" postures of Vertical Stance, Side-Step and Horizontal Leap, and may possibly be connected with the emergence of some sort of social order among the kittens.

Kittens are evidently strongly motivated to play with their brothers and sisters; pity the poor only child, a rarity among pet cats but commoner in farm cats where disease may carry off all but one of the litter. A single kitten will try to persuade its mother to play, and for the first four or five weeks she will put up with this. Some games, such as chasing the tip of her tail, are tolerated more than others, wrestling for example. As the kitten gets larger and more boisterous she may get quite aggressive towards it. At no time in its life will a single kitten receive as much social play as a kitten with even one sibling. Surprisingly, while it is still with its mother it does not seem to compensate by

spending any more time playing with objects or exploring its surroundings.

The long-term effects, if any, of being an only kitten, have not been measured. Losing the company of siblings at about eight weeks may result in quite a dramatic change in behaviour, however. A student working at Southampton University, Fiona Smart, watched seven kittens that had been homed singly, when they were between three and five months old, and compared their play with those of eight kittens that had been homed as sibling pairs. Deprived of the opportunity to play with other kittens, the singles spent more time playing with their owners and their children, and even when they were not actually playing they tended to be in the same room as one of the family members. They also spent more time, by comparison with the paired kittens, playing with objects around the house. It is possible that experience of playing with other kittens during the first five or six months could influence the way that relationships with other cats turn out later in life, but this has never been studied.

KITTENS EXPLORING

Curiosity is a characteristic of every kitten. They begin to explore their nests as soon as they can paddle themselves around, and as soon as they can walk they make short excursions into the outside world. At the same time, they seem to have an acute awareness of how far they have strayed from their nest, because they will often be six or seven weeks old before they venture more than a few metres away. Anything close to the nest that gives an opportunity for climbing will quickly become a favourite playground. Lucy's kittens quickly adopted a sofa beside their nest as their domain; if anyone was sitting on it that made their games even more exciting. As well as climbing all over it, they also delighted in burrowing under the cushions. Occasionally the whole litter would fall asleep under one of them, but luckily we could guess where they were and make a careful check before sitting down. Exploratory play by kittens has not been studied in any detail, but it presumably ensures that the cat's sense of balance and poise develops fully. Since in the wild it will undoubtedly expose kittens to more danger than if they stay in the nest, it must have some value that outweighs this disadvantage.

This kitten climbing-frame was built by Professor Patrick Bateson and Dr Paul Martin at the University of Cambridge, for their study of exploratory (locomotor) play. Seven litters of kittens were allowed access to the frame for half an hour every three days, from five weeks old until two months of age. The average amount of time that they spent climbing on the frame increased from just three minutes for the youngest kittens, to twenty minutes for the oldest. The mothers, who were with their litters throughout, were much less interested, spending only between one and five minutes on the frame, although they explored the frame carefully when they were first introduced to it. In the first few sessions, the kittens kept to the lower rungs, but as their skills improved, they gradually ventured higher and higher. The most skilful reached the top before the end of the experiment, but many of the clumsier ones never did. However, the occasional tumbles never resulted in a kitten hurting itself, and a fall was invariably followed by a further bout of climbing. The most daring kittens often belonged to those mothers that had spent the most time exploring the frame in the first place. This could either be due to the kittens imitating the mother, or there could be an inherited factor which indirectly makes mothers and their offspring more inclined to develop climbing skills.

KITTENS' "TOYS"

Moveable objects, including both small "toys", and larger items, such as curtains, are fascinating for kittens. First of all they will be investigated carefully, by looking, touching, sniffing and sometimes licking, until the kitten is sufficiently confident to include them in a game. Once this happens, the kitten has a complex repertoire of scoops, tosses, pokes and bats that keep the object moving, alternating with grasps in the front paws or in the mouth. Some of the patterns which the kitten uses in play with other kittens, such as pounces and chases, are also used towards objects. Biologists have noted that kittens play with objects for much longer at a time than the young of most other carnivores. The reason seems to be that the kitten keeps the object moving, most often by batting it with a paw, and that this sustains interest.

Young kittens usually prefer to play with other kittens than with objects, but social play wanes after they are three months old, and then object play may take over as the commonest type. From the age of about seven weeks, males play more with objects than females, although female kittens tend to be more active than males at this age. In mixed-sex litters, the females play with objects almost as much as males, but in all-female litters (which are thought to be uncommon) object play is slow to become popular. Kittens that are homed singly at eight weeks have little or no opportunity for social play after that, and although contact with new human companions may substitute to some extent, some of these kittens indulge in extra play with objects.

Although biologists like to divide play into neat "social" and "object" categories, the two frequently get muddled up, as one kitten is attracted by an object that is temporarily in the possession of another kitten. However, competition over objects is not an obvious feature of play between kittens, whereas puppies, for example, may spend hours quarrelling over a bone or an old sock. In these contests for possession, it is hard to avoid the conclusion that the object is not really the focus of the dispute, but rather that the two puppies are using it as a way of working out which one of the pair is dominant. A dominance hierarchy, or "pecking order" does not seem to be an obvious feature of adult cat society, which would explain why dominance contests are not a feature of kitten play.

WHAT IS ALL THIS PLAY FOR?

Biologists either find play fascinating, or tend to dismiss it as the figment of a sentimental imagination. The issue that underlies both these attitudes is a simple one. Most kinds of behaviour (feeding, drinking, sexual and maternal behaviour, aggression, territoriality) have fairly obvious functions at the time they are performed. Much of the behavioural research going on now is devoted to finding out the ways that different animals deal with these functions, and how these may have evolved. Play sticks out like a sore thumb when functions are considered. It costs energy (but not much – perhaps an extra 4 per cent), and it exposes young animals to risks that they would not be so likely to meet with if they stayed motionless in their nests. It has no obvious immediate function, yet it seems to be an essential part of a kitten's upbringing. As has already been mentioned, undernourished kittens do not play less to save energy, they play *more*.

Meredith West of the Indiana University has suggested that one function of social play may simply be to keep the litter close together, making it easier for the mother cat to find them all – play as an "invisible play-pen". This may be so, but most kittens' natural timidity away from their nest-site probably works just as well. Most of the other explanations revolve around the idea that play produces its benefits later in life. In other words, a kitten that does not play will turn out to be a defective adult. This

There are many influences that help a wild kitten to become a competent hunter. The important ones are shown as solid arrows, those that are probably important are shown by dotted arrows. Many of these processes interact; for example, if the mother brings in prey, the kittens may manipulate it themselves, or may hang back and watch their nestmates manipulate it, depending on whether they are genetically bold or timid.

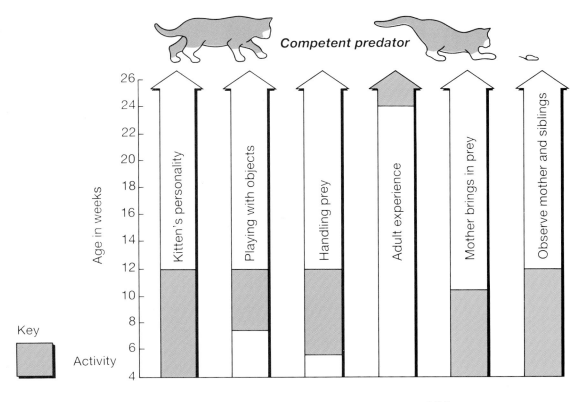

has proved to be a difficult idea to test. Because kittens play spontaneously, it would be almost impossible to prevent them from playing without depriving them of many other experiences as well. For example, hand-reared kittens often behave oddly later in life, but this may not be due to a lack of social play, it is more likely to be due to general lack of contact with other cats during kittenhood.

Because so much play looks like hunting behaviour, several attempts have been made to link the amount a kitten plays with its eventual prowess as a hunter. These links have been harder to establish than was originally hoped, and it now seems likely that kittens become good hunters primarily through contact with the prey brought back by their mothers, although play may also have a part in fine tuning those abilities.

With play in other species, dogs for example, social as well as hunting skills are being practised. We know now that adult cats which live in groups have a complex social life, so it is time we began to think about the role of play in the social development of kittens.

CHAPTER 6

Cat Chat

Compared to dogs, cats are rather undemonstrative creatures. If anything, they seem to be even more aloof with each other than they are towards their owners. Ten years ago, most people thought that cats were solitary, territorial animals that only needed to communicate with other cats during territorial disputes and in order to attract a member of the opposite sex for mating. Since virtually every other domesticated animal has been derived from a species that lives in groups with a social structure, the cat was thought to be an interesting exception to the general rule that only group-living animals can be domesticated. Some claimed that cats are not really domesticated at all. Although this statement may contain an element of truth, recent research proves that cats are capable of living in groups.

To be sociable, an animal has to develop a rich repertoire of ways to communicate with its fellows. Relationships have to be established and maintained to benefit both partners in some way. Aggression between group members has to be minimized, especially in an animal as well-armed as a cat, and replaced by some other, less risky, method of resolving disputes. In this chapter, the "language" of cats will be explained, as a necessary preliminary to examining their social life, because it is the "glue" that enables groups to stay together.

SMELLS – THE NOTICEBOARDS OF COMMUNICATION

In many countries of the world, the smells that human or animal bodies give off are regarded as, at worst, disgusting; at best,

(Opposite) Tail raised and quivering, a tom cat makes his territory by spraying urine backwards on to a prominent object.

they go unnoticed. We spend fortunes on disguising our own odours with more socially acceptable perfumes, some of which, paradoxically, contain components from the scent glands of animals. The very idea that an animal would communicate by odours seems odd to us. On the other hand, the extremely detailed information that we obtain from the aroma of food or drink shows that smell is a not unsophisticated sense. Although it is difficult to prove scientifically, it is safe to assume that the cat's nose is as well-educated as that of a wine-taster, but is sensitive to social smells rather than the bouquets of rare vintages.

Given that we are not ourselves accustomed to communicating by smell, it is worth considering why an animal would choose to do so. Smells are used widely by an enormous range of species, from insects to primates. Chemical communication is thought to be the most primitive method, since it is clearly a very similar process to the way that the different parts of animals' bodies co-ordinate their activities by means of hormones. For animals with less sophisticated nervous systems than those of mammals, chemical signals can be very reliable and effective. Many female moths produce minute amounts of a mixture of chemicals, known as sex pheromones, which they release into the air to attract males. Each species produces its own characteristic blend, and the antennae of the males are equipped with enormous numbers of specialized receptors, which respond only to the precise blend produced by the female of their own species. Many male moths live for only a few days, and have no time to learn what a female smells like, so a rigid, robot-like system suits them very well. The female can attract males from a very long distance, often up to 1 km (0.6 miles), so in that sense the system is efficient. However, she has to rely on the wind to carry her message, so a male sitting just 50 m (164 ft) upwind of her may never know of her existence (although males have their own strategies for finding females, such as zig-zagging up-and-down or across the direction of the prevailing wind). This example illustrates three of the main features of chemical signals: they possess great sensitivity (since the chances are minimal of the identical chemical being produced elsewhere in the environment); they can spread over large distances, even when produced by quite small animals, but the direction in which they spread is totally dependent on the wind; and, although they

are easy to turn on, they cannot be turned off instantaneously – odours hang around in the environment, and can betray the existence of the animal that emitted them for hours or even days afterwards.

Mammals with relatively few enemies can exploit this last property, and leave chemical messages behind them to provide other members of their own species with information about their identity and whereabouts. If a territory is large, it may be impossible for its owner to patrol its boundary more than once a day. If scent marks are left in the territory, they serve as a reminder to any intruder of who the territory-holder is. Chemical signals are therefore just as useful to solitary cats as they are to social cats. For a feral cat living in the Australian bush, ranging over an area of 1-2 sq. km (0.4-0.8 sq. miles), the occasional scent-mark may be all the contact he has with other cats, outside the breeding season.

Dogs, particularly male dogs, are keen scent-depositors and sniffers. Cats tend to be a little more subtle, but most pay a great deal of attention to scent-marking and sniffing at the marks of other cats. It is quite difficult for us to guess just how much information is transmitted in each scent mark, but we can usually work out what the purpose of that mark might be by recording the place and circumstances under which it was deposited.

Thankfully for those owners for whom litter trays are a great convenience, most cats squat while urinating and defaecating, and then bury what they have done. Even buried urine and faeces can often be sniffed out by another cat, but one purpose of burying is presumably to reduce the amount of smell produced. Young cats and neutered cats usually try to bury all their excreta, but entire adult males and females often leave their faeces uncovered, and spray their urine on to prominent objects, particularly if they are away from their home base. Toms do this more often than queens, and, if owned, will often spray indoors as well as outdoors. The habit is usually broken by neutering, although I have to say that all three of the neutered males that routinely visit my garden spray frequently. However, because they are neutered, the smell of their urine is not nearly so strong as that of the entire toms which visit Lucy, my female cat. Perhaps the presence of an entire female is the reason for so much spraying.

Spraying itself, for those who have never seen it, is unmistakeable. The cat backs towards the object to be sprayed, its tail held erect and its back slightly arched. While urine is being sprayed backwards and forwards, the tail quivers from side to side, possibly as a side-effect of the pressure needed to force out the urine. Some cat biologists have reported a version of this sequence which is complete, including the tail-quivering, except that no urine is emitted. Perhaps the cats' bladders were simply empty, but this "dummy" display is usually observed as part of a contest between two tom cats, so it may have ritual significance. Real spraying during a male-male fight is comparatively rare.

Mature males spray regularly when they are out hunting. They direct their sprays at obvious landmarks, presumably to add a visual cue, and increase the chances that another cat will actually sniff the mark and use the information in it. Favourite targets include the corners of buildings, hay bales, fallen branches, fence posts, grass tussocks and molehills, depending on whatever is available close to the "ideal" place for the mark. As well as marking their hunting ranges, toms also increase their rate of spraying when females are in oestrus. Females are also most likely to spray at this time, whether they are on their own or in the company of a tom.

Cats can evidently tell the difference between sprayed urine and urine delivered from a squat, and this has fuelled speculation that, in the sprayed type, the urine is simply a carrier for some other secretion, which may be the one that conveys the message. Male lions and tigers, which also spray, can inject the contents of their anal sacs into the spray to increase its odour. Domestic cats have anal glands, and these contain a small amount of pungent material that is occasionally discharged if the cat is very stressed. For example, a cat that is not used to being handled may empty its anal sacs on to someone who has to pick it up, perhaps for veterinary examination. This reaction is presumably purely defensive in function, and the smell, while disgusting, is not particularly like that of sprayed tom-cat urine. Tom cats have another pair of glands under their tails, which produce a pungent, clear liquid; this liquid may be a component of sprayed urine, but as yet this has not been proved. Two unusual chemicals, felinine and cysteine-S-isopentanol, occur in the urine itself. While neither has much odour of its own, once the urine has been sprayed they may both produce smells as they decompose.

If our knowledge of what goes into sprayed urine is sketchy, we know even less about how much information a cat can get from the smell of a spray. Toms are the most assiduous urine-sniffers, and they pay particular attention to the urine-marks of toms that they have never encountered before, sniffing these for half a minute or more. Part of this time is often spent testing the smell of the urine with the other olfactory apparatus, Jacobson's organ (*see Chapter 2*). Less attention is paid to the marks of toms that live nearby, and still less to any toms that live in the same social group as the sniffer. Females spend rather less time sniffing the same marks, but they also pay least attention to those produced by males from their own group.

This suggests that each mark indicates the identity of the cat that emitted it. This is tempting speculation, but not absolutely necessary to explain these observations. For example, it is known that the odour of urine is influenced by what the producer has eaten recently. Groups of cats that live together are likely to eat roughly the same food, which may not be the same as that eaten by cats coming from some distance away. Likewise, cats that live together are usually closely related, while those from far away are less likely to be so. If the odours are similar within families, this could provide a further source of variation. So the differences in the amount of sniffing could simply be explained by the degree to which the urine smelt familiar or unfamiliar.

However, it is now well established that dogs can memorize odours, for example those of people, and can use their recollections to distinguish between them, even when the emitters are identical twins. The proportion of the dog's brain that is given over to decoding smells is greater than it is in the cat, but even so cats probably can tell which urine marks were produced by who, and act accordingly. Unfortunately, this is one area where science has simply not caught up with the cat.

One problem is that cats do not behave very differently after sniffing a urine mark than they did before. If some marks – say those of toms that had recently defeated them in a fight – caused them to run away, whereas others did not, we could deduce something about the information that the cat was receiving. However, if urine marks affect behaviour at all, they must do so after a considerable delay, which means that cause and effect are difficult to disentangle. So, why do cats not keep away from the scent-marks of dominant individuals? The answer is probably the obvious one, that they are sniffing in order to store up information about the places that each cat has visited recently. A dominant cat will have visited a large number of places unchallenged, and should therefore have deposited the most scent-marks. It may also be possible for the dominant cat to be identified by the similarity between his own body odour and the smell of his scent-marks. This process can be seen in action in many other social carnivores; for example, the alpha-male in a pack of wolves will frequently stand stock-still, with its tail erect, and allow the subordinate members to sniff beneath it, to confirm his status.

In some of the older books on cat behaviour it is suggested that the spray-marks that cats make when away from home help them to space themselves out when hunting. A cat that comes across a fresh spray-mark will know that another cat has passed by recently, and will probably have disturbed all the potential prey in that vicinity. It is certainly true that cats can tell the difference between fresh and stale marks; different parts of the smell will evaporate at different rates, and some new smells will be produced by bacteria and other micro-organisms. However, biologists maintain that any signal must provide an advantage to the signaller, and this explanation only gives the advantage to the cat that picks up the message. Cats that did not spray as they hunted might not be detected, and could therefore gain an advantage over any cat that hunted, unsuccessfully, through the same area an hour later. That is not to say that cats never use the information in scent marks in this way, but there must be another reason for their production, one that favours the depositor of the mark. Another fact that tells against the "time-sharing" hypothesis is that cats tend to concentrate their spraying in the core of their hunting range. At the edges, where they are most likely to interfere with one another's hunting, the density of spraying tends to drop. Spraying is most likely an attempt to gain status, or territory, or both, and its main function may be different for solitary cats than for social cats.

We know even less about the functions of other scents that

cats produce. This is often the case for species which communicate by scent, sound and visual signals, and reflects a bias towards the methods of communication that we use ourselves. Because we have little intuitive feel as to how smells might work as vehicles for information, it is worthwhile describing some general principles before going on to discuss the cat's scents further.

The female moth, described at the beginning of this chapter, produces her scent in a specialized gland; just two or three enzymes convert common constituents of fatty tissues into a unique chemical blend that attracts the males of that species and no other. Such glands are rare in mammals. This is probably because they are warm-blooded, and a simple gland like that, exposed to the outside world, would form an ideal breeding-ground for bacteria. Rather than preventing infection, mammals have taken the route of exploiting micro-organisms and letting them produce odours for them. For example, if the anal sacs of carnivores are injected with antibiotics, they stop producing odour. The gland itself secretes food for the bacteria or yeasts within the sac; as a by-product of digesting that food, the micro-organisms produce the odour, and also keep out other, potentially damaging, infections. Skin glands, although less specialized than anal sacs, probably work along similar lines. Other sources of odour, such as faeces, invariably contain micro-organisms that contribute to the odour.

This partnership may have been inevitable, but it does raise serious questions as to how the animal controls the content of the message that it is trying to get across. If a new batch of micro-organisms invaded a particular gland, altering its smell, their mammalian host might lose its identity overnight! In the case of glands with enclosed sacs, the conditions within may be controlled sufficiently well to limit the range of micro-organisms that could survive to just a few species. Even so, the odour is certain to change slightly over a period of time. Therefore, it is very likely that the response of the animal that sniffs the odour will be entirely determined by experience both of previous encounters with that individual smell, and of other similar smells, perhaps those deposited by animals of the same sex and age group.

Some animals actively exploit this process, by deliberately

making their individual odours as similar to each other as possible. Many of the cat's carnivorous relatives appear to do this. European badgers, for example, possess a large pouch beneath their tails, which contains a strong-smelling waxy substance. By squatting down on to prominent objects, they can deposit blobs of this wax as territorial markers. In areas such as Britain, where badgers live in family groups known as "clans", the same wax is also deposited on the flanks of other members of the clan, mostly by the dominant male, although other members also contribute. In this way each badger is marked with a "clan odour", which the badgers check by sniffing one another's flanks and tail areas whenever they meet. The pouch contains numerous micro-organisms, and therefore the odour is likely to change slightly from one week to the next, creating a possible cause for mistaken identity. The badgers overcome this by occasionally engineering exchange of the micro-organisms between individuals. To do this, they back up to one another, and press their anal regions together. This is seen most commonly when one of the clan members has been absent for several days, during which there has been an opportunity for his odour to drift away from that of the rest of the clan. Group-specific odours of this kind have been suggested for cats, but have never been proved to exist.

Cats do not seem to have any scent-gland as large as the badgers', and although scents other than urine are undoubtedly used in communication, the messages they convey are unclear. The presence of "middens", communal defaecation sites used by several cats, may have some social significance, or they may simply reflect a shortage of sites suitable for burying faeces. Occasionally, a cat will deposit a pile of faeces on a prominent site, usually well away from its home base. Such piles are used by many animals, including, for example, otters, to mark territories. It is not known whether cats have this purpose in mind.

Cats also possess a battery of skin glands, most of which are probably there to produce chemical messages. The soft skin under the chin conceals the large submandibular gland; the hairs in this region may take up the secretion of this gland, and then transfer the smell when the cat rubs its chin on an object. There are glands along the sides of the mouth, and on each side of the forehead. Moving down the body, the tail is also equipped with

skin glands along its length, and there is a further glandular region at the base of the tail. This is often particularly active in entire toms, causing a condition called "stud tail", in which the hair becomes matted; in extreme cases infection of the gland can follow.

Biologists would like to know more about where these secretions are deposited, but none of them have much, if any, smell as far as human noses are concerned. Perhaps this is fortunate for the cat, for not many of us would give it house room if its secretions were as smelly as those of some other carnivores, such as the civet cat or the skunk! We can easily observe cats depositing these scents, as they rub the corner of a low table with their cheeks, or trail their tails across a chair leg, but at present we do not know why they do it. We do not even know if each one of these smells means something different, or whether they are all more-or-less interchangeable. Casual observations suggests that objects are often marked with the gland that happens to be most convenient. If it is something the cat is walking underneath, the head may be raised slightly, or the cat may perform a little jump, to touch the object with its forehead. Objects at head-height get attention from the glands at the corner of the mouth, while something that sticks up from the ground may be marked by the underside of the chin. Cats mark objects both indoors and outdoors, often along paths that they visit regularly. Tom cats may first mark with their cheek glands, and then overmark by spraying the same area with urine. Why this should be necessary is still a mystery.

THE BODY-LANGUAGE OF CATS

Nowadays, everyone is aware that a great deal of the communication that occurs between people goes on subconsciously. What we say is often no more important than the way we say it, and what our bodies are giving away about our intentions. Without a verbal language like ours, cats fall back on body language when they encounter one another. Many of the moves and expressions are so clearly related to their functions that we can easily deduce what the cat is "saying".

For example, during unfriendly encounters cats try to change the apparent size of their bodies to convey information.

(Opposite) Several glands on the head may be used to scent-mark objects, including the gland beneath the chin (shown), and those at the corner of the mouth and around the ear.

An attacking cat can make itself look larger, and therefore more formidable, by contracting the thousands of tiny muscles at the bases of its guard hairs. The coat sticks straight out all over its body, including the tail, which takes on the appearance of a bottle-brush. In preparation for the fight that may follow, the ears are usually pulled back slightly, presumably to reduce the risk of damage. A cat that wishes to avoid a fight will flatten its coat, flatten its ears, and press itself low to the ground, as if to say "I'm too small and weak to hurt anyone". It is actually placing itself at a real disadvantage, since by crouching it is unlikely to be able to launch an accurate biting attack. The contest may go no further than a prolonged bout of this kind of posturing, which will be broken when the submissive cat begins to slink away slowly, trying to keep an eye on the dominant cat all the while, since there is always a possibility that it may press home its attack. If it does, a chase will often result.

Cats rarely roll over on their backs to indicate submission, in the way that dogs do. This may indicate that the cat's aggressive signals are rather more primitive, and less ritualized, than

This defensive posture is more often seen when a cat is threatened by a dog than in cat-cat encounters.

the dog's. The roll, as performed by cats, is usually seen as part of play or sexual behaviour, or in some individuals, a greeting behaviour towards the owner.

The "scalded cat" posture, beloved of cartoonists, but more properly known as the arched-back posture, is usually provoked by a sudden danger, such as an unfriendly dog. The tail is fluffed out and held vertically or in a hoop-shape, and the back is arched, as if the front legs were trying to escape backwards and the back legs forwards. These contradictory tendencies may be because the cat cannot decide whether to attack or flee, and so momentarily does both. However, overall the posture looks as if the cat is trying to increase its apparent height, which may have been an effective deterrent to some important enemy at some point in the cat's evolutionary history.

If these are the main competitive messages conveyed by the cat's body language, many shades of meaning can be added by the way the head and ears are positioned. A submissive cat may be able to avoid a conflict simply by studiously avoiding eye contact with an aggressor. Superficially, it looks as if the submissive cat is ignoring, or even has not noticed, the other, but if eye contact does occur, the fight will often escalate very quickly. The ears are pulled back to indicate readiness to attack, and pressed down and back, out of harm's way, to indicate readiness to defend. Ear positions can be altered much more quickly than body postures, so much of the posturing during aggressive encounters involves small movements of the ears, which can be tried out to determine the opponent's reaction.

Tails are potentially even more expressive than ears. There can hardly be a single cat owner who has not watched in fascination the twitching of the tip of a cat's tail, and wondered what it might mean. Sadly, science has paid little attention to these movements. Apart from the relaxed tail, the main tail postures are the friendly vertical tail, which will be discussed at the end of this chapter, the lashing aggressive tail, and the submissive tail that is tucked between the legs. During fights, the tail may also be curved like a croquet-hoop, with its tip pointing down at the ground, perhaps another size-increasing gesture. But there are many variations on these broad themes, so the tales told by tails must be many and various. For the moment, only fellow cats can understand them.

The cat on the right shows its confidence by sitting, ears forward, and staring straight at the other cat which pulls its ears back and shrinks away to avoid a fight.

CAT CALLS

Fights are one of the few occasions when cats make much noise; the others are before and during sex, and when demanding attention from an owner. Indeed, considering the cat's superior sense of hearing, it is surprising that they do not make more use of vocal communication in their day-to-day lives. Some other social carnivores, mongeese for example, have complex repertoires of calls which convey all manner of shades of social meaning. Groups of cats that are not particularly sociable towards people, such as farm cats, go about their business remarkably quietly.

Cats are probably more vocal at the beginning of their lives

than at any other time. Kittens maintain contact with their mother by a variety of special calls, the loudest of which is the distress call that was mentioned in the previous chapter. Inexperienced mother cats seem to understand what kittens are by the noises that they make. Blue-eyed white cats, which are often deaf, are also often inattentive mothers, presumably because they have difficulty in reacting to their kittens. The mother calls her kittens using a "chirrup" form of the trill, performed with her mouth closed. Each mother must make a slightly different sound, because by the time that they are three weeks old, kittens can tell the difference between their own mother's call and that of a stranger.

More evenly matched, these two cats are both trying to increase their apparent size by fluffing up the hair on their backs and tails.

The other main type of closed-mouth sound is the purr, which kittens begin to perform at just a few days old. From then on, and for the rest of the cat's life, purring can be triggered by all kinds of circumstances, as Martha Kiley-Worthington, working at Sussex University, found when she fitted cats with throat-microphones. It occurs in obvious circumstances, such as when a cat is sitting on a person's lap, or nursing kittens. It occurs during friendly greetings between cats, but is also performed by cats that are on their own, for example when they are rubbing on objects, rolling on the ground in a warm familiar environment. Some cats purr spontaneously as they are dropping off to sleep. So it seems natural for a cat to purr when it is "content", which may mean when it is, or may want to be, in contact with another friendly cat. Conversely, Dr Kiley-Worthington found that cats are unlikely to purr when they are intently occupied with something in particular, such as hunting, searching for a mate, or in the presence of an unfamiliar or aggressive cat. Unfortunately, this neat picture of what does and what does not cause purring is shattered by an occasional occurrence in veterinary surgeries of purring by cats that are in pain, perhaps following a road accident, or after surgery. People have suggested that this may be a way that the cat has of distracting itself when it is otherwise helpless to control its pain. However, it is unlikely that we shall ever know what is going through a cat's mind on such an occasion.

Purring is a strangely mechanical kind of sound to be made by a mammal, and there has been a great deal of speculation as to how it is made. Any serious explanation has to take account of the cat's ability to purr almost continuously, with only the faintest of pauses between inhaled and exhaled breaths. One of the more bizarre ideas was that vibrations in one of the main blood vessels in the chest were somehow amplified by the windpipe and air spaces in the skull. How these could be turned on and off at will was never fully explained. It is now certain that the sound is made by the vocal cords, where all other vocalizations originate. The sound is produced as they vibrate, pulled to and fro by muscles in the walls of the voice-box (or larynx). These muscles are controlled in turn by a group of nerves that generate their own rhythm, switched on or off by other nerves coming from the brain. Because this rhythm is generated locally in the throat itself, each cat will have its own purring frequency which it will not be able to alter very much.

Loud sounds are generally only used by cats in a sexual or aggressive context. To produce the required volume, these are all made with the mouth open. The aggressive calls, the growl, yowl and snarl, are all made with the mouth held rigidly in one position. The growl has the lowest frequency; some cats are capable of making such a loud, low-pitched rumble that it sounds as if it should come from a much larger animal. This is the vocal equivalent of the "fluffed-up" aggressive posture, making the cat seem to be bigger than it really is. The yowl, or caterwaul, can be performed in combination with the growl, or on its own. Typically performed by duelling males, its pitch usually rises and falls like a siren. The snarl is a harsh, more vocalized call, starting with an abrupt intake of breath and ending with an "-ow" sound. All of these aggressive calls are performed while the face muscles are tensed, presumably because the cat has to be ready to bite its adversary at any moment.

If the attack is pressed home, one cat is likely to emit the pain shriek, which is probably defensive in that it appears to be designed to startle the attacker into loosening its grip. The other defensive sounds – not really vocalizations – are the hiss and the spit, the meaning of which must be unambiguous even to other species, let alone to another cat. Have you ever guessed why most cats hate the noises made by aerosols and bicycle pumps? These must sound enough like a hiss to induce real terror.

The sexual calls of both male and female are also loud, but more like human speech, in that they begin and finish with the mouth closed. They are quite unlike human speech in that they are uttered partly while the cat is breathing in, and partly when he or she is breathing out. The male sexual call, or mowl, is made to females that are in season, and to other males that may be courting her.

Apart from purring, the sound that most people associate with cats is the miaow. Every language has some representation of this type of call:

The English cat *mews*, the Indian cat *myaus*, the Chinese cat says *mio*, the Arabian cat *naoua*, and the Egyptian cat *mau*. To illustrate how difficult it is to interpret the cat's

The spectograms below provide a visual representation of two cats' miaows. In each box the sound begins on the left and lasts for about half a second. The height of the coloured areas indicate the notes that make up the miaow, high-pitched towards the top, low-pitched towards the bottom. The sound on the right is the typical, two-syllable miaow. The sound on the left is an unusual, low-pitched, stuttering greeting call.

language, her "mew" is spelled in thirty-one different ways, five examples being maeow, me-ow, mieaou, mouw and murr-raow. (Mellen *The Science and the Mystery of the Cat.*)

Cats will occasionally miaow at each other in an apparently friendly way. The trill, or greeting-miaow, is also used in this context, but it is difficult to know what the purpose of either call is in cat-cat communication. On the other hand, almost all cats use both trills and miaows when conversing with people. In some cases, a whole vocal language seems to develop between cat and owner, based on variations on the miaow. Mildred Moelk, a psychologist and life-long observer of cats at her home in Rochester, New York, distinguished three types of trills and four types of miaows in her ten-year-old female cat. The trills, all with the mouth closed, were different for the purposes of greeting, calling and acknowledgement. Varied shades of miaow were used to indicate demands, begging demands, bewilderment and complaint. She only ever heard the acknowledgement trill and the bewilderment trill from her own cat, but she claimed that the rest could be distinguished in other cats as well.

Although no proof is available, it seems likely that cats develop their trills and miaows because they are encouraged to do so by their owners. A cat may learn that a long drawn-out miaow

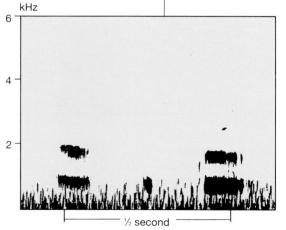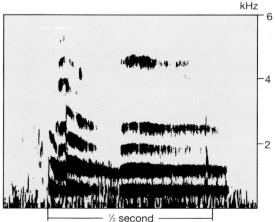

Mewings (adult)

prompts its owner into hastening with the preparation of its meal. A trill performed by a closed door encouraged the owner to open it. In this way the cat builds up an association between making the sound and getting something that it needs, a simple case of instrumental learning (*see Chapter 3*).

Why use miaows and trills, rather than some other signal?

Tails raised to indicate mutual friendliness, two young feral cats exchange mutual head-rubs (see page 161).

159

First of all, a sound is probably a better way of gaining the attention of a human than a gesture. When we want to get someone's attention, we call them first and wave afterwards, to confirm who uttered the call. The sort of call that the cat can use is probably dictated by its rather limited vocal abilities, and the fact that all the other calls have a distinct meaning to other cats. If a cat yowled to be let out, it might find a tom ready to fight on the other side of the door. There may be another, more subtle reason for the choice of sound. The miaow is made like a word, starting with a consonant and continuing with a complicated vowel-sound. It sounds roughly the way it is written. It is probably not too fanciful to suggest that cats miaow at us because they are trying to imitate our speech. As described in the previous chapter, kittens learn well by imitating other cats, so why not copy people as well? If a parrot can learn to imitate the sound of the human voice, why shouldn't a cat also try?

CATS' CARESSES

Most cats love to get close to people they know, curling up on laps and purring in contentment. They may even give their owners the occasional lick, as they would when grooming another cat. This is a kind of communication, at the simple level of cementing a friendship. Most cats also run around their owner's legs, some giving just the gentlest caress with the tip of their tail, others using every inch of their cheeks, flanks and tail as well. We will discuss these displays again in the later chapters, but they are undoubtedly an important part of cat-to-cat communication as well.

Cat-to-cat rubs can occur in a number of ways. Two cats may walk past one another, rubbing as they go, or they may walk side-by-side in contact, rubbing their heads together, up and down. Sometimes just the heads touch, sometimes heads are rubbed along flanks as well, or flanks along heads. Occasionally, even, tails may be intertwined. These variations have not been investigated by biologists. It is not even known whether the primary purpose of mutual rubbing is just to touch the other cat, or whether scents are being transferred at the same time. When two cats rub their faces and ears together, it seems inevitable that they will exchange some of the scents that they use to mark objects, but we cannot yet be certain whether this makes any real difference to either of the cats. This display is very important to relationships between cats (*see Chapter 7*), and we now know how cats signal that they are ready to rub.

CATS' CONVERSATIONS

Dr Sarah Brown, who works with me at Southampton, has studied the rubbing displays of cats, both between pairs of cats, and between cats and their owners. As a general rule, the cat raises its tail to the vertical position before approaching its partner. Cats raise their tails on other occasions, but may not rub because the other cat (or person) may have indicated an unwillingness to accept the rub. Why should such a signal be necessary? Why do cats not just go ahead and rub without announcing their intentions? The explanation is that cats seem to pick as partners for rubbing, cats with whom they have a slightly one-sided relationship. They may therefore need to signal to the target of their rubbing that their intentions are friendly, in order to avoid being rebuffed. Sometimes both cats will raise their tails, in which case the rubbing become mutual and more intense. Like everything about the cat, these conversations are enigmatic, but through them we are beginning to get a glimpse of how cat society operates.

CHAPTER 7

Cats Together

*I*f you own two or more cats, there is a good chance that they will be friendly to one another. Unfortunately, my own are not; Splodge's only interest in Lucy is to deliver the occasional cuff when she sits on his favourite window-sill. However, when she comes into season, he sometimes makes a half-hearted attempt to court her, despite his having been neutered when he was a kitten.

Pet cats that are sociable might only be so because of encouragement from their owners. To see whether cats can be spontaneously friendly, we must examine those that are not pets and are at best only tolerant of people. Over the past fifteen years or so, it has become increasingly clear that cats are perfectly capable of living in groups where the conditions are right, but under other circumstances they are also capable of living alone. They are not alone in this; many other animals are now known to be able to adjust the size of the groups they live in to suit the prevailing conditions.

As a general rule, female mammals have to ensure that they can find enough to eat, and also enough to support their young until they are old enough to fend for themselves. If they did not, they might live their whole lives without producing grand-children, and therefore all their genes would be lost. Male mammals usually put far less effort into raising young than females, so the number of grandchildren that they produce is usually limited by the number of females with which they can mate. Two males might co-operate if by doing so they could more than double their success as fathers. Among the cat family, only male lions and cheetahs are known to do this, probably because in other species the females live too far apart. The females have to spread themselves out because in any one place there is only enough food to support one family. This is probably the reason why, apart from lions, none of the wild members of the cat family have females that live together. However, this general rule has apparently been broken by the domestic cat.

Our cat's ancestor, the African wildcat, is both solitary and territorial. Some domestic cats live like this. In the Australian bush, where prey is scarce, a female cat's territory may be as large as 1-2 sq. km (0.4-0.8 sq. miles). On farmland, more productive in small rodents, up to five cats may be found in every square kilometre, even when they obtain all their food by hunting. Higher densities of cats only occur when part or all of their food is provided by people. The only exceptions to this are the aggregations of cats found around seabird colonies on isolated islands (see Chapter 4), and these are themselves somewhat unnatural, because the cats have been put there by people, and have few other predators to provide them with competition. On farms, up to fifty cats may share the farmyard and the surrounding farmland, hunting the hedgerows, or hanging about near the farmhouse waiting for a handout. Occasionally, even more cats than this can be packed into a small area, usually in a town or an industrial site; the record for density seems to be held by Ainoshima, a Japanese fishing village. Because cats can be a nuisance or even a health hazard in these numbers, such sites are not as common now as they may have been previously. Cats are extremely flexible in adapting to how far away the nearest cat may be. This is not to say that a cat that had once lived in a solitary life could instantly change to living on a crowded urban site (crowded by cats, that is). However, its offspring probably could, showing that there is nothing written into the genes of the cat to stop it from becoming sociable when the conditions are right.

Whatever the overall density of cats, from the Australian outback to a Japanese fishing village, the amount of space occupied by each female must be large enough to provide her with a consistent supply of food for her and her kittens. Little is known about how a female demonstrates her ownership of what is normally a very large territory. Presumably scent-marking plays a major part, because the distance to be covered on a regular patrol of her boundaries would leave no time for hunting. Scent-marking may also be used to make sure that cats which share a hunting range avoid one another.

Mature males usually have much larger ranges than females, no matter what the overall density of cats in the area. This cannot be determined by their need for food. On average, their ranges are three-and-a-half times larger than those of females. If they needed three-and-a-half times as much food as a female, they should, based on the requirements of other animals, be more than five times heavier than females. They are heavier, certainly, but only by about 50 per cent. In fact, food plays little part in determining how far they roam. Because they have no role in the raising of kittens, they are simply interested in gaining access to as many females as possible. Outside the breeding season they may only occupy a small area, around a good source of food. In the mating season, they may suddenly start to roam over a much wider area. For example, Paul Chipman of Manchester Polytechnic found that in an area of 0.25 sq. km (0.1 sq. miles) in Manchester, England, there were no less than nineteen entire males. Their normal ranges varied from less than one hectare, to six in the case of one mature and apparently dominant individual (no other tom was ever seen to go near him!). When the only two entire females in the area came into season, they attracted the attentions of eight and ten toms respectively, and many of these must have travelled from well outside their normal ranges. Such journeys must inevitably bring males into conflict with one another, and in rural areas it is sometimes possible to distinguish between dominant males, which are able to expand their ranges in the breeding season, and subordinate males, which are either prevented from doing so, or perhaps do not even try, knowing that they would be unable to stand up to the dominants if they did.

On farms, male kittens are usually rejected by their mothers when they are a few months old, but they may stay in the vicinity for another year or so. While they remain close to their mother or their mother's social group, they rarely become sexually mature. This reduces the probability that incest will occur; similar inhibitions occur in other social carnivores, such as wolves. Alternatively, as they mature, they may be driven away by older males. They are then forced to become nomads, keeping their distance from other cats, until by chance they happen upon a vacant territory, or can challenge an existing territory-holder. Ideally, they will end up as the sole male in a group of females, like Tom, the male at the farm where David Macdonald carried out his pioneering study of co-operation between queens, described on page 173. In cities, they may roam widely, competing for access to the few unneutered females with other toms, both resident and nomadic.

SEX AND REPRODUCTION

The campaigns to prevent unwanted kittens by neutering all cats during adolescence have had a great deal of success, especially in towns and cities. Because of this, many cat owners never see the sexual behaviour of males of females. Unneutered males do not make particularly good pets. Neither their habit of spraying pungent urine whenever the opportunity arises, nor their generally belligerent nature, are particularly endearing. Stud cats kept by breeders generally have to be kept enclosed to separate them from other cats except when they are needed for mating. Because they are denied the company of their own species, they may become very attached to their owners, but this attachment is really a product of the artificial situation in which they have to be kept. Let them run wild, and that is exactly what they are likely to do.

When they are not in season, unneutered females behave much like neutered pets. As soon as they come into oestrus, their personalities can change overnight. If she was born in the spring, a well-fed female will generally come into season for the first time late on in her first winter, although this can be delayed for up to a year in cats that live wild or on farms. The first sign of a change is restlessness, coupled with more rubbing on the furniture than is usual. Out of doors, rubbing on prominent objects such as gateposts will also increase, and the female will urinate more frequently and in new places. She is more likely to spray her urine now than at any other time. However, any passing tom cat that notices these changes, perhaps guided by a change in her scent, will still be rebuffed, or even attacked. Acceptance of

The tom cat grasps the female by the scruff of her neck as he prepares to copulate.

toms does not even suggest itself until the next stage, when she begins to make the characteristic female sexual call, a wail that rises and falls in pitch. This is a clear indicator to males that she will soon be ready to mate. She will soon begin to roll over on her back spontaneously, and a touch at the base of her tail will cause her to crouch, as if ready to copulate. She will purr, stretch, and make treading movements with her front paws, all signs that

mating is imminent. If she is able to get outside, there will almost certainly be a tom cat in attendance by this stage.

She will normally allow him to sniff her, and he will do so repeatedly, curling back his top lip to show that he is assessing her condition using his vomeronasal organ (*see Chapter 2*). Initially he may not be allowed to approach any further, but soon she will adopt the lordosis position, her rump lifted in the air, and her tail

As soon as the tom withdraws, the female lashes out at him.

curled to one side. This is the signal for the tom to mount, but before he does so, he grasps the female in his jaws by the scruff of her neck. This presumably helps to subdue her by triggering the scruff reflex (*see Chapter 5*). Copulation itself is usually brief, and as the tom pulls away the queen will usually cry out in pain and turn on him, spitting and scratching. However, an experienced tom will not be put off by this, but will stay nearby and groom himself while he waits for her to become receptive again. This will probably occur within the next ten to fifteen minutes, when she will offer herself to him again.

Her scream of pain is real, because the tip of the tom's penis is studded with backward-pointing barbs. This apparently sadistic behaviour on the part of the tom is, however, his way of ensuring that conception occurs. Unlike most female mammals, cats do not ovulate spontaneously. Instead, the stimulation of mating itself leads to a surge of hormones, which cause mature egg-bearing follicles in the ovaries to burst and release their eggs into the oviducts. Usually several copulations have to occur before this process is triggered.

About twenty-four hours after mating, the sperm left behind by the tom reach these eggs, and fertilization can occur. If the female does not mate, the follicles simply shrivel up, without releasing any eggs, and a few weeks later she will come into season again. Note that it is the act of copulation, not fertilization, that starts the first stages of pregnancy. A female mated by a neutered tom will behave as if she is pregnant for up to six weeks, although her eggs have not been fertilized. Some breeders keep such a tom in order to prevent their queens from coming into season every fortnight or so when they are not required for breeding. Alternatively, seasons can also be blocked by contraceptive injections. If a queen is allowed to call repeatedly, she will soon lose condition and permanent damage to her reproductive system can follow.

MALES

When male cats are scarce or cat territories are very large, the female's long period of receptiveness may simply give the male enough time to locate her. If there are several males in the vicinity, a female will often be courted by more than one. She will then have a choice of fathers for her kittens. In this situation, her strategy should be designed to make sure that she produces strong, healthy offspring. She can use her extended period of receptiveness to test the strength and stamina of the males that have found her.

These tests take two forms, as Olof Liberg discovered when he studied rural cats living in a military training area in Sweden. First, the female will copulate between ten and twenty times a day, over the four to six days that she will accept males. This frequency of copulation exhausts all but the most robust of males, and so these are the most likely to father the kittens. Second, if there are several males present they will have to compete with each other for the female's favours. Dr Liberg noticed that each time he watched a female that was in season, one of the attending males achieved all the copulations. This male, who was typically about four years old, stayed close to the female, usually within 1 m (3.2 ft), and if she moved away, he would follow her closely. He would spray urine frequently, presumably to reinforce his status. Other males usually stayed further away, and would be threatened or even attacked by the dominant male if they tried to get close to the female. Aggression between these bystanders was rare. Probably there was little point in competing for second place.

However, the bystanders were sometimes given a chance to mate by the female, who would attempt to give the dominant male the slip by unexpectedly rushing away from him. Presumably this was another test of his stamina and determination. If a bystander did obtain temporary control of the female, he was usually ousted by the dominant male before he could mate with her. Sometimes the dominant status is held by the same cat throughout the whole of the queen's season. I have noted this myself on one occasion with my own cat Lucy. When she comes into season her normal timidity evaporates, and instead of staying close to home as she normally would, she leaves the garden over and over again in search of a mate. She must be courted elsewhere, because we rarely see toms on these occasions. However, her second litter was probably all sired by the same tom, a white cat with black markings who took up temporary residence in our garden for three or four days. Presumably because she no longer needed to seek out a mate, Lucy stayed

(Opposite) Scarred from innumerable fights, while maintaining his former status as a breeding male, this tom cat is reduced to a shadow of his former self.

close to home, while he guarded her from the attentions of other toms. Every so often he would detect that another was nearby, and would immediately launch an attack. Scuffles and yowls in the undergrowth would follow, and on every occasion he returned to Lucy's side victorious. Two months later she gave birth to three male kittens, each with the same amount of white as he had had. Although this is no guarantee that he had sired them all, the indications were that his strategy had paid off.

Among the Swedish cats observed by Olof Liberg, some males would monopolize a particular female for a day or two, but then leave her, allowing another male, often one that had previously been a mere bystander, to take over. The dominant male may simply have become exhausted, or he may have detected another female in season nearby, and decided to hedge his bets. None of the takeovers resulted from the dominant cat losing a fight. Even within a single year, some males could be dominant with one female, and a bystander with another. This may be partly due to the extra "confidence" that a male usually has when operating on his home ground. It is tempting to think that the female cats were also expressing their individual choices over which males they wished to become dominant.

When females live in large groups, as they sometimes do on farms, males behave rather differently. There are probably too many females for any one male to attempt to monopolize them all. Some males spend most of their time within the group, but these tend to be youngsters that rarely mate. If they can, the older breeding males visit several farms in turn, seeking out females in season at each, and attempting to monopolize them for a day or two. At any one farm, many of the females will be closely related, so it is sensible for a tom to try to sire kittens in a number of different families, to make sure that at least some survive. This fast and loose way of life takes its toll, however, and within a few years these toms are usually reduced to mere shells of their formerly virile selves.

Occasionally within large groups a male and female will pair up, and stay together even when she is not in season. This is much less exhausting for the male than the life of a rake, but he is counting on his chosen female producing surviving kittens. If she turns out to be a less than perfect mother, or is simply unlucky, none of his offspring may survive.

Why should a female accept the attention of more than one male? Because she copulates many times, it is perfectly possible for each kitten in a litter to have a different father. She may be hedging her bets. If none of the males that court her emerges as the strongest, it may be sensible for her to allow each to sire part of the litter. There is also a more sinister reason, that is known to apply to lions, and possibly to cats as well. Male lions that take over a pride of lionesses will usually kill all the cubs in the pride. These cubs are no relatives of theirs, and they need to bring the lioness back into season as soon as possible so that they can sire litters of their own.

Biologists cannot agree about the frequency of infanticide in domestic cats. Few of them have actually observed it happening, although it has been seen in the Indian wildcat, but there are plenty of anecdotes indicating that domestic kittens on farms may be killed by strange toms. David Macdonald, of Oxford University, observed one horrific incident on a farm in Devon. Four female cats, three mothers and one grandmother, had set up a communal nest among hay bales for their nine kittens. One afternoon, when none of the adults was in sight, a strange wild male appeared from out of the undergrowth. He headed straight for the hay-bales, leaped into the nest and swiftly dispatched six of the kittens with bites to their heads. Their frantic cries brought their three mothers running, and the murderer fled. Each mother carried one of the survivors away and hid them deep in the haystacks. Their father turned up a couple of hours later, having probably been visiting another of his harems at a nearby farm. Too late, he sniffed all around the nest, before indulging in an orgy of urine-spraying all around the yard. Presumably he was trying to obliterate the smell of the stranger.

If actual infanticide is rare, many queens with kittens behave as if it might happen at any time. They can become antagonistic towards any cat, but particularly towards males, while their kittens are helpless in the nest. This may also tie in with their habit of sometimes mating with more than one tom. If none of the toms can be certain which of the kittens are their own, and which have been sired by rivals, then they should all leave the kittens alone to ensure that their own progeny survives. Co-operation between females forms the core of domestic cat society, and it is to them that we turn next.

THE PRIDE IN THE FARMYARD

Feral cats congregate wherever there is a reliable and sufficient source of food. This may be a garbage dump in a fishing village or in a dockyard, a farmyard, or anywhere where cat-lovers put out food for strays. For many years, biologists dismissed these groups as mere aggregations around food, like animals round a salt-lick or waterhole. Then, almost simultaneously, David Macdonald and Peter Apps at Oxford, Jane Dards at Southampton, Olof Liberg in Sweden, and Masako Izawa in Japan discovered that these aggregations have a real structure, based around alliances between females.

Usually most of the females in a group will be related to one another, perhaps a grandmother, her daughters and grand-daughters. Occasionally unrelated females will join together. For example, the four females whose nest was raided by the strange male, as described above, consisted of two unrelated mother and daughter pairs. Females rarely move from one group to another, although groups that get too large will split into two. Males, on the other hand, may roam from group to group continually, or attach themselves to one group for just a year or two before moving on. Females in a group band together to defend a communal territory, and, most remarkably, to help one another with rearing kittens.

David Macdonald's Devon farm cats are typical. When his study started, there were four cats on the farm; a male, Tom, a female, Smudge, and their daughters Pickle and Domino. Tom ranged widely, and spent only about one-third of his time with his family. When he was at home, all the females were affectionate to him, Pickle so much so that he occasionally had to rebuff her with a hiss or a cuff. They preferred to snooze curled up with him, or if he was not there, Domino would usually sleep next to her mother. Each cat came and went as it pleased, and when they were not in the farmyard they invariably kept to themselves. Unlike the lion, domestic cats never hunt in groups or even in pairs. Their prey is not large enough to need two cats to kill it, and two cats hunting close to each other would simply scare away each other's game.

Strength in numbers does pay off when there is a territory to defend. Three other cats lived near the farm; a female, White-tip, her son Shadow and daughter Tab. Smudge, Pickle and

(Opposite) A family group of farm-cats.

Domino would attack any or all of these on sight, particularly Whitetip. Tom was more selective. Shadow was nearly always the target of his aggression, presumably because a young male could be a future threat to his status. Immediately after an encounter, Tom would spray urine to blot out the smell of the intruder, and would sometimes be rewarded by a flank-rub from one or other of his females. Some incidents that happened in the farmyard, involving either Shadow or other foreign males, suggested that the females were capable of persuading Tom to come to their assistance. For example, on one occasion a large feral male appeared, and tried to force his attentions on Smudge. If she had been in season she might have given him more of a welcome, but she was not, and her screams of rage quickly brought Tom on to the scene. Together they attacked the stranger, and drove him away. As if to thank Tom, Smudge rubbed on him repeatedly, and even courted him briefly. All the time that these four cats lived together, the behaviour of the females suggested that they were keen to retain Tom as their protector. This exclusive arrangement does not occur in larger colonies; perhaps it is difficult for more than three or four females to agree on their ideal mate.

Family ties help in large colonies. Once farm kittens are ready to be weaned, they must be brought to a feeding-site, where they will have to compete with adults. If mothers move their kittens at this stage, they often try to relocate near to the food. Gillian Kerby, studying farm cats in Oxfordshire, found that less than half the litters born and raised well away from the farmyard survived. As a result, some of the females had left no surviving descendants after seven years of breeding. The best area, around the food in the farmyard, was monopolized by a few families. Survival rates were much better here, with only 15 per cent of litters perishing. As the central families grew in size, so some of the younger female members were unable to stake a claim to a nest-site in the farmyard itself. They had to raise their litters in less favourable places, such as hedgerows, where the kittens were exposed to the weather and to predators. If any kittens did survive to weaning, they would then have to make the perilous journey into the farmyard in order to feed with the rest of the colony. Shared territories, if they contain valuable resources, are literally a matter of life and death for farm cats.

MIDWIVES AND NURSING

If cats only co-operated to enable them to share food, it is unlikely that their social life would ever have become particularly interesting to biologists. However, cat families are much more close-knit than this, and the most dramatic evidence comes from the assistance that females give each other when they are producing kittens. The fullest co-operation occurs when two or more litters arrive within a few days or weeks of each other. Given that outdoor cats breed mainly in the spring, this is fairly likely to happen anyway, but Olof Liberg in Sweden found that females within a group synchronized their seasons much more closely than changes in the weather could account for. The same thing happens in group-living females of other species, such as our own; when women live together for several months at a time, their menstrual cycles become synchronized.

Cat breeders have known for many years that related queens tend to be interested in one another's litters. This was always dismissed as a distortion of normal behaviour brought about by human influence, until David Macdonald and Peter Apps recorded the help that their farm cats gave each other when kittening. Early one May, Pickle produced three kittens in a nest buried deep within a straw-stack. She was apparently unaware that the back wall of her nest had been replaced by a sheet of glass, and that on the other side of the glass crouched a BBC film crew. For two-and-a-half weeks she raised her kittens on her own, just as if she had been a solitary female. Then, without warning, her sister Domino joined her in the nest, and promptly began to deliver the first of five kittens. All the while Pickle groomed her, and as each kitten appeared she helped Domino to remove its membrane and cut its cord. She also ate most of the afterbirths; if these provide essential nourishment for the nest-bound mother, as was suggested in Chapter 5, then Pickle was cheating her sister! Both mothers cleaned the new kittens, and then settled down to suckle all eight. They never seemed to discriminate which kitten belonged to which mother, despite their differences in age and size. Tragically, this particular story did not have a happy ending, because all eight kittens died from cat 'flu, a common scourge of farm cats that is often aided and abetted by the damp British climate. But when Pickle and Domino's mother Smudge produced a single kitten two weeks later,

Pickle in particular spent a great deal of time helping Smudge in her nest. Both Pickle and Domino brought Smudge food that they had caught. Later on, when Smudge was hunting for the kitten, they occasionally reverted to being her kittens themselves, and stole some of the food she brought back. Overall, however, they were probably more of a help than a hindrance, and the kitten, a male, grew well. In view of the fate that had earlier befallen his nephews and nieces, he was given the name Lucky.

There is also a happy ending to the tragic story of the kittens attacked by the marauding male. Their mothers were in fact Smudge, Domino and Tab, Tab and her mother Whitetip having been accepted into the group at about the same time that Tom departed, his place being taken by another male, Ginger. Of the three kittens that survived the raid, one had originally belonged to each of the mothers. They were hidden in three separate nests for a while, but within two weeks they were back together again. Just as Domino and Pickle had shown no discrimination in favour of their own kittens, so this litter was raised as a team effort.

Communal rearing of kittens is probably commonplace on farms and in other places where cats gather round reliable food-supplies. So far, biologists have not been able to prove that it actually benefits the kittens. It must do under some circumstances, or the habit would have died out, but it does have obvious disadvantages, as illustrated by the fate of Pickle and Domino's litter. Kittens born outdoors are susceptible to disease and accidents, and many of these are just as likely to kill a whole litter as just one or two individuals.

It has been suggested that mothers could protect their relatives' offspring against disease by allowing them to suckle. This is possible because milk, and particularly the special form of milk called colostrum that is produced in the first few days after the birth, contains antibodies produced by the mother. These antibodies are absorbed by the kittens and give them some immunity against diseases. If one mother's colostrum was rich in antibodies against, say, enteritis, and her sister's contained antibodies for 'flu, they could give all their kittens some form of protection by allowing all of them to suckle from them both. This is still a theory, however, and it does not seem to have worked for Pickle and Domino. Furthermore, when cat viruses were

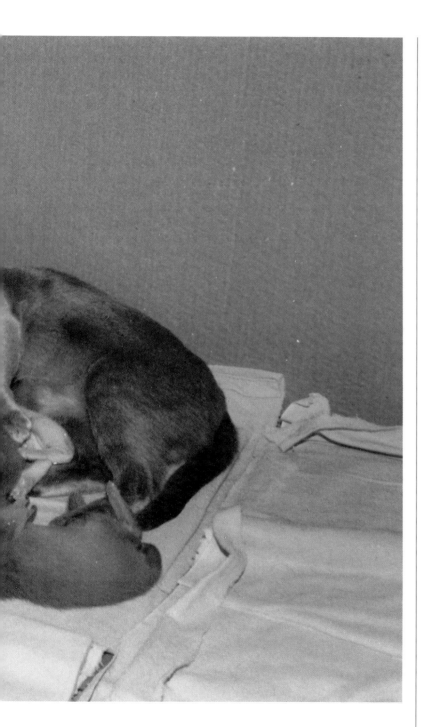

Related females commonly care for one another's kittens.

introduced to Marion Island off the coast of South Africa in an attempt to control the feral cats there, the survivors tended to be those that lived alone. This also argues against communal nursing providing protection against disease.

The rarity of infanticide in domestic cat litters may provide another clue to the benefits of communal litters. Several mothers can keep a much better eye on their young than one can, particularly when they are in the process of moving from one nest to another. In this way, they may be able to thwart the evil intentions of roaming males.

Other biologists think that communal rearing of kittens is just an accident, bringing no great advantages or disadvantages. Immediately after the birth of her kittens, the mother's disturbed hormone balance causes her to become much less aggressive to other cats. This is probably part of a mechanism to ensure that she does not regard the kittens as her rivals, but rather something to take care of. In the unusually high densities of cats that occur on farms or around other permanent sources of food, these hormonal changes are likely to be synchronized in queens that give birth within a few days of each other. This will make them more trusting than usual, and so more likely to give birth in the same nest. This attitude will also help them to accept the prolonged period of time they must then spend together to raise their kittens successfully. This lowering of barriers may be a by-product of domestication: Dr Reay Smithers' two African wildcats, described at the beginning of Chapter 1, were normally friendly towards one another, but became very territorial and aggressive towards one another when they had kittens.

FOSTERING

Whatever its benefits to the cats, communal nursing can be a boon to those overstretched and un(der)paid people who rescue cats and kittens. In the warm, dry, clean conditions of a cat shelter, kittens are less likely to become ill than they would outdoors. When we rescued eleven feral cats from beneath school buildings in Winchester, three of the females were found to be pregnant. At the shelter where they were taken, all the litters were pooled by their mothers soon after they were born, and all the kittens thrived, and were eventually found homes. In this case, the three mothers were probably all closely related, but with a little persuasion mother cats may also raise kittens that are not their own, making fostering possible. Outside their nests, some mother cats are able to distinguish between their own kittens and strangers. Within the nest, they seem to be much less choosy, and if one or two kittens are slipped in among their own, they may be accepted almost immediately. Some cat rescuers are good at picking out particular queens with "earth-mother" qualities, and can trick them into wet-nursing one litter after another for a whole breeding season.

Two years ago, the Cats Protection League sponsored Fiona Smart, a student at Southampton University, to record the progress of some fostered kittens. One that she found was actually being fostered by a pair of queens, Pippa and Pepper, who had eight kittens between them already! When the study started the orphaned kitten was already three weeks old, and Pippa and Pepper's own kittens were about five weeks. Pepper was doing most of the nursing; Pippa had produced six of the eight, and was obviously in poor condition. Once she had re-covered her strength, helped by huge meals provided by her carer, CPL member Margaret Cooksey, Pippa took over feeding three of her own kittens and one of Pepper's, while the orphan, three of Pippa's and the other one of Pepper's still pre-ferred to suckle from Pepper. There was never any indication that either queen remembered which kittens were their own, and the two weeks' discrepancy in age between the orphaned kitten and the others did not seem to matter either. Needless to say, the kittens seemed equally oblivious of blood ties when choosing partners for play.

Fostering is preferable to hand-rearing, which is fraught with problems for kittens. It is difficult to avoid upsetting their stomachs, since cat's milk has a very different balance of nutrients to cow's or any other milks. They are much more likely to survive if they can suckle from a cat, even if only for the first few days of their lives. If a hand-reared kitten does thrive, it should be kept in contact with other cats, so that it can learn what being a cat is all about during its socialization phase (two to seven weeks of age, described in Chapter 8). Cats that are kept away from their own kind early in life tend to grow over-attached to people, and this may lead to behavioural problems. They are also unlikely to ever become friendly with other cats. The females rarely mate successfully, and have difficulties with raising their own kittens. Since rescued cats are neutered as a matter of course, the latter deficiencies are unlikely to be important for domestic pets. Unfortunately the same difficulties apply to many of the other species of small cats, many of which are endangered in the wild. The success of captive breeding programmes can therefore stand or fall on producing the right conditions for the females to raise their own young.

NEUTERING

Discussion of farm cats and cat shelters leads inevitably to the fate of feral cats. There may be upwards of a million cats in the United Kingdom alone that have never been socialized to people, and live a semi-wild existence. They are often unhealthy and ill-fed, particularly where they are breeding freely. Reactions to the sight of these cats vary from those of the dedicated feeders who spend all their spare cash on cat food, to those who dislike them and call for their extermination. The latter is virtually impossible to achieve, but indiscriminate feeding simply encourages more breeding and more unhealthy cats. Probably the most humane answer, espoused by the Universities Federation for Animal Welfare and the Cat Action Trust, is to capture the cats, treat them for any parasites and any injuries they may have, neuter them, and let them go again where they were caught. Many of these colonies will be co-operating family groups, and hopefully they will continue to defend their territories even after they are neutered. This is by no means a foregone conclusion, however. In theory, if cat society is built around reproduction and maternal care, it might break up soon after neutering.

Accordingly, Sarah Brown, a postgraduate student at Southampton University, and I have been studying the behaviour of several groups of cats that have been neutered and re-released, some on their original sites, one at a new site. After neutering, the behaviour of males changes slowly. Basically, they become more tolerant of one another, although this could be because, with no females in season nearby, they have little to compete over. Young males do not mature, of course, and they

can form alliances, as young females usually do. Membership of the groups was remarkably stable, on a par with breeding colonies. Neutering seemed to have made the cats more tolerant of outsiders, however, at least in so far as sharing food was concerned. Favoured resting-places may still be defended.

Social behaviour may help neutered cats to cope if they have to be confined in a shelter. Sometimes it is impossible to find places to release feral cats after neutering, and if they have grown up without human contact they are unlikely ever to make pets. The alternatives are then euthanasia or a life in captivity. Debby Smith, a student at Southampton University, and I looked at the relationships that had developed between cats that had lived together in a shelter for up to seven years. Cats that had been there for less than a year showed few signs of sociability. While not obviously aggressive, by and large they kept themselves to themselves. Some of the cats that had been there for over a year remained solitary, but many had become quite affectionate towards one or more of the other cats. Three sisters, who may have sparked off this friendliness, would often sit together, and an unrelated tabby ex-tom would usually join them. The three sisters were all black, but once Debby had worked out how to tell them apart, she discovered that the relationships between them were not all equivalent. Two of the sisters rarely interacted, and never sat next to each other. If all three were together, then the third one was always in the middle! There was no clue as to what had originally caused this rift, but it presented an amusing parallel to some human behaviour.

CAT SOCIETIES

Social life implies social communication. Alliances have to be formed and maintained; differences of opinion have to be resolved. In many animals – wolves are a good example – competition between the members of a pack is resolved by a dominance hierarchy. Each animal has a status within the pack, and real aggression only occurs when a change in the hierarchy is imminent. Positions in the hierarchy are often obvious, even to a human observer, because the animals perform displays which indicate and reinforce their status. Often it is only the highest-ranking animals that breed, while the subordinates assist with the rearing of the young. The problem facing biologists who study the domestic cat is that under normal circumstances no such hierarchy can be determined, either in the males or the females. (If cats live at a very high density indeed, the males do form some sort of loose hierarchy, but there is no evidence that this has any bearing on the number of kittens that each fathers.) Without much of a theoretical framework on which to hang the working of cat society, it has proved difficult to interpret everything that cats say to one another. I suspect much remains to be discovered about many of the subtleties that underlie the social order in colonies of cats.

Whenever a colony is examined, it is clear that each cat reacts differently to each of the others. In a small colony, this probably implies that all the cats recognize one another as individuals. In larger colonies, consisting of several families, one cat may know some of its neighbours as individuals, but others may simply be identified by their sex, age, and which colony they belong to. As a general rule, females in the same group interact most with males and kittens, and rather infrequently with each other. Infrequent interaction may simply indicate familiarity, so that each female knows how the other is going to behave without having to communicate anything. Young cats between one and two years old interact with each other quite frequently, but less often with adult females, and rarely with adult males.

Of course, what each cat says is likely to be more important in determining a relationship than the sheer number of conversations that occur. In some interchanges the intention of both parties is clear, for example in fights or sexual behaviour. As we have seen already, sexual behaviour is not particularly highly structured in cats, and aggressive behaviour is fairly rare within groups, though it is generally the rule between groups. Two other types of social behaviour may, however, tell us a little more.

Cats that are most relaxed in each other's company will often lie or sleep in contact with one another. They are renowned for their cleanliness, and so it comes as no surprise that when they are sitting in contact, they often groom each other. If this was done purely for the sake of cleanliness, we might expect it to be confined to the head and neck, which a solo cat has to deal with by the indirect method of wiping these areas down with a

Mutual grooming seems to cement the relationships between friendly cats.

fore-paw. Yet when cats groom their friends, they do not restrict their attentions to these areas. Flanks are a favourite. The overwhelming impression is that mutual grooming is a way of cementing relationships, just as it is in many primates. If this were so, we might expect cats would be selective about whom they groomed, even among the cats with whom they regularly sat. To quote one example from research done by my own group, Debby Smith recorded the number of times her group of three black sisters and one tabby male groomed each other. The females groomed the male three times more often then they would groom any of their sisters. Perhaps they were trying to keep his affiliation to the group, just as the farmyard cats Smudge, Domino and Pickle did with Tom.

There may also be an exchange of social information when two cats rest together. Sarah Brown has noted that before they do so, they often sniff one another, particularly on the head and around the tail. It seems unlikely that they are checking the other cat's identity at this stage; presumably, each has already identified the other before they even approach, and to pick the wrong partner could have painful consequences in the competitive world of the farmyard. The sniffing must logically be a way of discovering what scents the other cat has picked up recently. These would mostly be undetectable to our noses, but the cat's acute sense of smell can probably pick out all sorts of detail. For example, it should be possible to detect what the other cat had eaten for its last meal from smells lingering on the fur of its head. Traces of odour from the environment – aromatic plants that the cat brushed against, bonfire smoke that blew past – should provide clues as to where it has travelled recently. Perhaps most significantly, the odour of any other cats which it had recently rubbed on might be detectable. In other words, before they settle down together, cats probably catch up on their form of gossip!

Within a colony, not all cats will rest together, and fewer still will groom each other. Something else is needed to maintain the cohesion of the group. This seems to be the role of the mutual rubbing display, described in Chapter 6. Sarah Brown has shown that rubbing rarely occurs before cats sit down together, at least in neutered colonies. In breeding groups, rubbing probably maintains bonds between individuals with different positions in cat society. When kittens rub on their mothers, they almost always start the process; mothers may rub back, but they rarely rub first. Females rub on tom cats, who hardly ever rub back. Rubbing is therefore usually performed by the weaker to the stronger, and in other social animals such displays are often used to indicate that the weaker acknowledges the status of the stronger. However, the cat's rubbing display cannot be compared to the cringing display of the subordinate dog or wolf. Cringing can be spontaneous, like rubbing, but unlike rubbing it is often a response to aggressive threats from the dominant cat. If rubbing and aggression ever occur together in an interaction between cats, it is the rubbing that comes first. Presumably the rubbing cat has just misjudged the way its rub would be received. Rubbing is never used to pacify an aggressor. Are cats too proud to beg, or are they just different to other social animals? We need a better understanding of cat society before that question can be answered.

A SOCIAL HISTORY

It is something of a mystery how cat society started. The domestic cat's close relatives and ancestors, the wildcats *Felis sylvestris*, are invariably solitary, territorial animals. David Macdonald has observed them in Saudi Arabia, not far from where domestication originally took place, living alongside feral domestic cats and scavenging around garbage dumps. The feral cats lived in groups; none of the wildcats did. It is just possible that group-living wildcats are still to be discovered, but in the meantime it seems likely that social life and domestication go hand in hand. My own version of this important part of the cat's history goes as follows:

The first steps towards today's domestic cat came when African wildcats began to cluster around grain stores in Egypt, drawn by the plentiful supply of rodents there. Something about their makeup made them tolerant of humans, and this gave them the edge over other similar predators that might otherwise have shared in the good hunting. Seeing that the cats saved their grain, the Egyptians encouraged them, perhaps supplying sheltered nest-sites. They would probably also have taken newly-weaned litters and tamed them as pets. To begin with,

(Below) The African Wildcat: a solitary hunter. It must have become tolerant of people during domestication.

the cats presumably established territories in and around the granaries, just as they would have done if they had been hunting in the bush. As more cats crowded in, disputes became frequent, and this would have limited the number of rodents that could be killed.

The advantages to be gained from sharing a territory with one's close relatives must have been overwhelming, and so the tendency for females not to leave their mothers at adolescence would have evolved quickly. However, even at the end of this process, cats have retained their ability to go back to the lifestyle of their wild, solitary ancestors, thereby producing the great flexibility in social behaviour that we see in cats today. The other facet of this process is the growing relationship with humans, and this is the subject of the next and final chapter.

CHAPTER 8

Of Cats and Men

O ver the whole course of their history, cats have maintained a very flexible relationship with humans. From the temple cats of ancient Egypt to the modern apartment-dweller, they have been able to sacrifice their free-ranging instincts for the benefits of guaranteed food and shelter. Yet, just a few metres from the exclusive apartment blocks where their pampered cousins live, there will probably be

Five feral cats at a hospital, resting together soon after dawn before dispersing to hunt in the grounds.

semi-wild cats, scratching out a meagre existence by scavenging and hunting.

The potential for contrasting lifestyles to exist side-by-side was first made clear to me when I assisted with a survey of the cats at a partly disused hospital. In the grounds and the basements lived about seventy feral cats, almost all neutered. None of these would submit to being touched, and most would vanish at the first glimpse of a human. (Although for some reason many were much more approachable at first light in the summer, before the daytime staff of the hospital began arriving for work. We turned this to our advantage for our survey, because it meant that the cats were much more easily identified at 5 a.m. than at any other time.) Inside the hospital lived another, totally separate population of cats, one or two to each ward. These were let out for exercise once or twice a day, and if this coincided with one of our patrols they would approach us to be made a fuss of, but we never saw even the briefest contact between these cats and the ferals. They must have been aware of each other, through the scent-marks that each deposited in the same areas, but otherwise they lived in two completely separate worlds. Yet both were, in their way, essentially dependent upon humans. The ward cats were provided with food and shelter directly. The feral cats were fed copious amounts of waste food and also some specially-bought cat food put out by cat-lovers, and they relied on the hospital staff's tolerance to permit them access to the warm, dry basements that sheltered them through the winter. Without these handouts, both intentional and unintentional, it is doubtful whether the hospital grounds would have provided enough food or shelter to support more than one or two cats.

This degree of flexibility is unprecedented among domesticated animals, and indeed some experts place the cat in a different category – that of exploited captives, alongside such animals as the Indian elephant. The truth must lie somewhere in between, but it is easier to regard the cat as a special case, to be contrasted rather than compared with our other companion animals. In Europe, it is doubtful whether the cat would have survived at all if it had not been able to adopt a semi-independent existence while it was suffering centuries of persecution from the Christian church. Some biologists think that this persecution is the primary reason for the lack of variety in the European breeds of cat. All the ancient pure breeds, the Siamese, Burmese, Angora, Persian and Abyssinian, come from non-Christian areas. Derivation of pure breeds requires that cats are kept closely confined over many generations, and these circumstances seem to have been lacking in Europe until recently, when such breeds as the Devon Rex have appeared. Most of the other modern "fancy" breeds have been derived in America.

Until recently, many cats were kept with at least an eye to their abilities as pest controllers, but ever since the time of ancient Egypt they have also been treasured as companions, and as approachable representatives of the animal kingdom. Cats uniquely combine the qualities of intimacy and independence, bringing a flavour of the wild into our lives that no other animal can match. Most dogs are just too highly modified by domestication to give much of the flavour of their ancestor, the wolf; and although one or two breeds, such as the Siberian Husky, are honorable exceptions, they are far from easy to keep. One of the many disadvantages of the modern trend towards urbanization is the loss of contact with the wilderness where humans evolved. Keeping a cat can remind us of those origins, and may even help to satisfy some of the instincts that we bring from our hunter-gatherer origins. There are of course many more practical attributes that people value in the cat, such as independence, cleanliness, reliability in returning home, and lack of aggression towards people. Yet none of these really explains the appeal of the cat. They merely explain why cats make acceptable house-guests. The fascination that cats hold for people lies deep in the human psyche, and is a subject worth a book of its own. For the rest of this chapter, I will attempt to provide a biological focus on cat-keeping, and its converse, a cat's-eye view of people.

WHAT DO WE DO FOR CATS?

Cynics often remark that cats display the ultimate in cupboard love. It is certainly true that a cat is unlikely to stick around for long if its owner fails to feed it. By contrast, many dogs are almost pathetically attached to their owners, and will tolerate a horrific level of neglect, as the photographs put out by the animal welfare charities prove so eloquently. A brief comparison of the ecology of wolves and of feral cats will suggest why this is so.

(Opposite) Splodge resting in the treehouse that the author built for his son. (See page 196.)

When wolves have cubs, the core of their territory is their den, where the cubs, their mother and other adult "baby-sitters" spend much of their time while the rest of the pack hunts. This division of labour means that the site of the den can be chosen to provide maximum protection for the precious cubs. It does not particularly matter if the hunting grounds are not close by, because food can be brought back to the den for the young and their carers. For the cat, a reliable source of food close to the den is absolutely essential, so even neutered house-cats will instinctively position their territories around their food-bowl. This does not mean that a cat's bond with its owner is driven solely by a full belly. It simply means that cats feel that they cannot afford to stay somewhere where they cannot find food. Unfortunately in some cats this instinct extends not just to the quantity and reliability of the food, but also to its quality. As a result, a cat fed adequately but perhaps only a couple of times a day in one household can sometimes be tempted to move elsewhere by highly palatable food that is supplied on demand. In our surveys of cat owners around the south of England, we have heard many stories of cats being (willingly) kidnapped by neighbours. Finding a cat prospecting for alternative food and shelter, it seems alarmingly easy for people to ignore its well-fed and cared-for appearance and assume that it is a stray. We always ask owners where cats came from, and the number that fall into the "just turned up" category suggests that cats transfer from one household to another more often than is perhaps realized.

Because feeding cats is a conscious act, it is easy to forget that they probably value us just as highly because of the shelter our houses provide. The cat's desert-dwelling ancestors had to cope with both the heat of the day and the cold of the night. The domestic cat's kidneys, capable of producing much more concentrated urine than our own, show us that it is still very much an animal of the desert. Because of this, it is much less well suited to the damper temperate climates where the majority of cat owners live. Feral litters are often smitten by droplet-borne viruses that would be far less devastating in a dry climate. Most cats instinctively hate rain and most other forms of water, unlike most dogs. The Turkish Van cat, a truly instinctive swimmer, and the occasional cat that will sit in a puddle and play with the water are the exceptions that prove the rule. In a survey of feral

.

cats in Brooklyn, New York, it was found that shelter, rather than food, was the primary factor that regulated the population.

Simple observation of our own pets will show that resting-places are an important resource for them also. Splodge, my long-haired male cat, has a favourite windowsill that he will defend against all the other cats in the house. Comparing it with all the other windowsills in the house, it has three features which probably make it valuable. First of all, it is wide enough for his not inconsiderable bulk, although when he falls asleep one limb or another will often dangle untidily over the edge. Second, there is a warm radiator immediately below it, so it is always cosy. Third, the window gives an uninterrupted view of several front gardens and the street in between, much of which seems to be disputed territory for the neighbourhood cats. His other favourite places have similar combinations of warmth and visibility. One is an old greenhouse where he retreats on cold, sunny days, or when there are kittens in the house. The other is my younger son's tree-house, draughtier than the other places and therefore used only on warm days, but unrivalled as a look-out.

So, which is the more important, shelter or food? Obviously both are essential. Except for mothers with kittens, they do not have to be in exactly the same place, although if they are far apart and there are other cats nearby, moving between one and the other might be a hazardous business. Science still has no answer to the question of just how much importance cats place on having a selection of suitable resting-places to choose from. Millions of pounds and dollars must have been spent over the years on the development of today's succulent cat foods, but our understanding of what a cat looks for in a shelter is still sketchy. However, anyone who has to leave their cat alone while they are out at work, and is worried that it might be tempted to stray, could do worse than making sure that it has a selection of warm, secure places to sleep.

DO CATS SEE US AS MOTHER-SUBSTITUTES?

In his book *Catwatching*, Desmond Morris states categorically that cats see us as surrogate mothers. This has been the commonly-accepted view for many years, and it fits in well with general theories about domestication. Most domesticated species, and the dog is no exception, are thought to have undergone a process called "neotenization". This results in the animal retaining some of its juvenile characteristics into adulthood – in other words, it never really grows up. The "toy" breeds of dog are familiar examples; their skulls and skeletons are like those of newborn wolves in both size and shape, and they behave rather like wolf pups all their lives, with one essential exception: they are able to breed from about one year onwards. A wolf, which grows many times larger than a toy dog, and whose behaviour matures in all kinds of ways, does not become sexually mature until it is about two years old. Incidentally, neotenization has also occurred in the evolution of wild animals, without any intervention from man. The classic example is the axolotl, an amphibian that is effectively a tadpole that becomes sexually mature without ever leaving the water. Hormone treatment of young axolotls can reverse the neotenization. They develop lungs, and turn into what was presumably their original adult form, a land-dwelling black and orange salamander.

The domestic cat is a little smaller than the African wildcat, but otherwise its skeleton shows no unequivocal signs of neotenization. As described at the beginning of this book, this very lack of change has made it difficult to distinguish whether prehistoric remains of wildcats show any signs of domestication. Evidence for neotenization must therefore be looked for in behaviour rather than in physical appearance.

The classic behaviour pattern that seems to confirm that cats are just overgrown babies is familiar to most cat owners. It is the kneading action of the forepaws, often accompanied by purring and a faraway look in the eyes, that cats often perform on soft rugs or clothing. This looks just like the actions of a kitten, rhythmically treading its mother's teats to stimulate the flow of milk. It is known that kittens do this spontaneously, even when no milk is forthcoming. A farm or feral cat that is weaned by its mother, and therefore progresses from nursing to hunting for itself, presumably loses the habit of "kneading". A kitten that has been weaned by its owner has simply transferred its dependence from its mother to its owner, and therefore continues to display the same pattern. However, in adult cats it is no longer confined to feeding occasions, but occurs whenever the right stimuli (a fur-like texture, possibly coupled with warmth and some olfactory cues) are available.

So, do cats simply see us as surrogate mothers? My personal opinion is that they do not. The following sections are mostly conjecture, just one way of looking at the scanty evidence that is available. Hopefully research will eventually help us to decide, one way or the other.

WOOL-SUCKING, CHEWING AND EATING.

Some cats do more than just knead on their owner's woollens and purr. They may go further in treating the fabric as if it was a teat, and start to mouth it or suck on a protruding thread. Some will do this to garments that are still being worn by their owner; some seem to anticipate this by drooling and dribbling whenever their owner picks them up. Over-attachment to the owner is often claimed to be the cause of this enhanced degree of infantile behaviour, but this has never been studied scientifically. Wool-sucking is not confined to any particular breed or type of cat.

Wool-chewing and eating can have much more serious consequences than just sucking, but is largely confined to Siamese, Burmese and other oriental breeds of cat. This may possibly start with wool-sucking, but the cat quickly progresses to chewing and then actually eating 'the wool. Once this habit is established, other fabrics, both natural and man-made, may be added to the menu. Sometimes the habit is only expressed sporadically, but other cats will eat their favourite fabric whenever they can get access to it.

In a survey that Peter Neville and I carried out of owners of wool-eating oriental cats, many reported extensive and expensive damage. To add to the cost, veterinary attention is sometimes required when the cat's gut becomes blocked after a particularly large quantity of fabric has been ingested, although small amounts can pass through without any ill-effects. Surprisingly, most owners value these cats so highly that they are prepared to put up with the cost. Only a few have had cats euthanized because of this problem.

Because it is breed-specific, it must have some kind of inherited basis, but environmental factors are needed to trigger it.

From the survey, Peter and I concluded that many cases first appeared soon after the cat had moved from one home to another, whatever the age of the cat. Other cases seemed to occur spontaneously when the cat was between six and eighteen months old, i.e. probably at puberty. The trigger is therefore most likely to be related to stress, either that of being displaced to a new environment, or encountering hostile cats when the instinct to set up a territory first asserts itself. Stress associated with being confined in a small space may account for the prevalence of wool-eating in cats that do not have access to the outdoors.

Once established, the habit seems very difficult to break. Some cats will only eat fabrics when their owners are out

(Above) Wool-sucking is a widespread habit among the oriental breeds, but can also occur in "moggies".

Others will blatantly drag their current favourite item to their food bowl and take alternate mouthfuls of fabric and cat food. The latter practice has probably prompted the idea that wool-eating cats are trying to increase the amount of roughage in their diet.

Some have been treated by being fed a mixture of chopped wool and cat food, but the effectiveness of this method is unknown. Neutering, recommended by some vets, appears to have little effect on wool-eating, although it does of course have other benefits, particularly for cats confined indoors. The only reliable method seems to be to deny the cat access to all tempting fabrics, although this may be difficult if its attention then switches from clothes to upholstery!

WHY DO CATS RUB AROUND THEIR OWNERS' LEGS?

The "kneading" display is of course not the only behaviour that cats perform towards us. Some cats hardly ever perform it at all. There are several other behaviour patterns that cats direct towards their owners, and these also need to be accounted for.

My wife claims that the only reason that Splodge tolerates any of us is because we feed him. He is particularly good at picking a moment when she is busy to wind himself in and out of her legs, his tail raised high. He is most likely to do this when he is hungry, but he has often run straight past his food bowl to get to her, and when he is put back there, he usually eats without further ado.

Because this display is frequently seen before feeding-times, many people think of it as a food-soliciting display. Yet, every day, Splodge, like thousands of other cats, demonstrates that this is nonsense. Whenever Splodge meets my labrador retriever, Bruno, he performs exactly the same display. He even waits at the end of the road for Bruno and I to return from a walk, and more often than not will choose to rub round Bruno's legs before paying any attention to me. In the time-honoured tradition of all labradors, Bruno is not in the habit of giving up any of his food to a cat; in fact, he will steal Splodge's food at every opportunity. I have seen other cats rub on dogs, and doubtless there are cats on farms and smallholdings that rub on farmyard animals.

The rubbing display is, to all intents and purposes, identical to that performed by one group-living cat to another, as described in Chapter 7. In colonies that consist of cats of both sexes and a range of ages, young cats are more likely to rub on older cats than *vice versa*, and females are more likely to rub on males than males on females. The oldest and largest individuals, the mature toms, almost never rub on another cat. Although we still do not understand its full significance, this is undoubtedly a status-related display, performed towards animals (individuals or species) to which the cat has been socialized when a kitten. Splodge will rub on me and members of my family, and on Bruno; we are all familiar to him, we are larger than he is, and he was socialized to both people and dogs when he was a kitten. This rubbing display has no direct connection with feeding, nor does it indicate that cats look upon us as mother-substitutes; they merely regard us as in some way superior. It is not even a product of domestication. As described in the opening paragraph of Chapter 1, Dr Reay Smithers' hand-reared female African wildcats greeted him by rubbing. This suggests that wildcats hand-reared by ancient Egyptians would have done the same thing, helping to build the bond between people and the cat that eventually led to domestication. It also confirms that the choice of target for the display is determined by socialization; these wildcats would have been strongly socialized to Dr Smithers when he handled them as kittens. He certainly had some difficulty in persuading them to mate with a captive male wildcat, so they probably thought of themselves as more human than cat.

The rubbing display seems to be so important to the cat's view of people that biologists have begun to study it in detail. Claudia Mertens and Dennis Turner, at Zurich University, were the first to record that rubbing is stimulated by a reply from the human participant. A friendly cat will usually approach any person, familiar or unfamiliar, who is sitting quietly by themselves, and will probably offer them a single rub. If the person continues to sit quietly, the cat will quickly lose interest. If, on the other hand, the rub is replied to with stroking or talking, the cat will probably repeat the rubbing sequence over and over again. Sarah Brown, working with me, has found that talking and stroking may also induce the cat to cheek-mark nearby objects, as well as repeatedly rubbing on the person. The significance of the

Most pet cats rub around their owners' legs (above), but many will also rub on other animals they are familiar with, as shown by the author's cat Splodge, going to rub on his labrador retriever (below).

scent-marking of objects is not entirely clear, but it looks as if the cat is attempting to reinforce its rights to a territory that it is sharing with the person.

Another observation made by Dennis Turner of Zurich University in Switzerland tends to confirm the idea that cats behave towards their owners as if they were superior members of their social group. When observing spontaneous encounters between cats and owners in their own homes, he found that interactions

If socialized together early in life, the traditional mistrust of cat and dog is easily broken down.

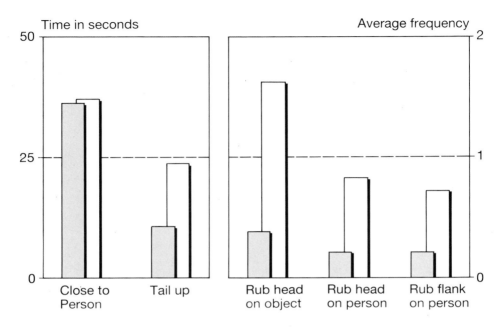

Key

Familiar person
ignores the cat

Unfamiliar person
strokes and talks
to the cat

that were started by the cat lasted longer, on average, than those started by the owner. The more enthusiastic the greeting by the owner, the shorter the interaction turned out to be. In cat society, friendly interactions are usually initiated by the inferior (younger, smaller) animal. Our pet cats presumably behave in the same way towards us, and by forcing ourselves on them we may be breaking one of the most basic rules of cat etiquette. Dr Turner's finding suggests that if we wish to extract the most from our relationship with a cat, we should let the cat make the first move as often as possible. Once the cat has started the conversation, gentle reciprocation by the owner will prolong it, to the satisfaction of both participants.

DO CATS NEED OUR COMPANY?

Cats see us as an intimate and important part of their social structure; they don't simply exploit us for the food and shelter that we provide as cynics maintain. Perhaps they are not very demonstrative of that relationship, but then feral cats that live in groups do not interact very frequently either. One way of testing this point of view is to compare cats that have different choices of partners for interaction; specifically, the differences between cat-human interactions in single-cat and multi-cat households. In a single-cat household, the cat can only interact with people. In a household with several cats, each can choose whether to interact with a cat or with a human. Some interactions are by their nature unique to one of the two possible combinations. Cats do not pick each other up; people cannot appreciate most of the olfactory signals deposited by cats. However, cats perform their rubbing displays on people and cats alike. While observing a large sample of Swiss households, some with just one cat, some with two or more, Dennis Turner discovered that several cats living together were, on average, less likely to rub their owners than single cats were. Unfortunately, he did not report the extent of cat-cat rubbing in the multicat households, so we cannot tell to what extent this interacts with cat-human rubbing.

One of my own students, Fiona Smart, compared the play behaviour of eight kittens homed as sibling pairs with seven homed singly in households with no other cats. She found that the kittens in the pairs played with each other a great deal, and correspondingly less with objects and with people. There are two possible explanations for this result; one is that people who deliberately choose to have two kittens at once do so because they enjoy watching them play together, and correspondingly play with them less themselves. However, the result also suggests that single kittens compensate for their lack of a partner of the same species by eliciting more play from people. A great deal more research is required to provide a definitive answer, but at present it looks as if cats value social contact with their owners. They may prefer cats as partners for interaction, but that may be simply because two cats speak the same language. If we could learn how to answer them more aptly, we could probably put ourselves in an equal footing.

WHY DO CATS BRING THEIR PREY HOME?

In *Catwatching*, Desmond Morris accuses cats of a kind of schizophrenia. One minute they may be treating their owners as mother-substitutes, treading away on their clothes to stimulate an illusory flow of milk. A few hours later, the same cat may bring in a freshly-killed mouse and deposit it at its owner's feet;

An experiment (opposite) carried out by Colette Hartle at Southampton gave us a fortuitous confirmation that interaction from a person directly stimulates the rubbing and scent-marking. She was examining the differences that might result from the person being a stranger, compared to someone who was familiar to the cat (all the human subjects were female, between fifteen and twenty-three years old). By chance, the cats spent almost exactly the same amount of time close to the stranger when she was allowed to respond as they spent close to the familiar person when she was unresponsive. Rubs and scent-marking were much more frequent with the responsive stranger. This disproves the other possible explanation for the increased rubbing and marking: that they take place automatically whenever the cat gets close to a person, and that the talking and stroking merely keep the cat nearby for longer.

Morris considers this to be the equivalent to a feline mother bringing home food for her kittens. To me, it seems unlikely that the same cat could regard its owner as its mother under one set of circumstances, and its kitten under another. So why do cats bring their prey home?

Most instances must be just the expression of normal hunting behaviour. A hunting cat will often drag its prey into cover before eating it, to avoid attracting competition from scavengers. The dangers of eating out in the open are illustrated dramatically by the cheetahs that hunt the open plains of East Africa. Cheetahs may be fast, but they often catch prey that is too heavy for them to drag away, and a group of hyaenas may bully the cheetah off its kill and consume most of the meat. The most secure place for a domestic cat to bring its kills is probably its owner's house, and so it is not surprising that it should try this once or twice. What is less easy to understand is why cats continue to bring prey home even when their owners apparently discourage it. Perhaps in some cases the discouragement is tinged with admiration for the cat's prowess as a hunter, and the cat reacts to the latter rather than the former. If the cat's motive is food-sharing, then there is no reason why it has to regard its owner as a kitten. Incidences of friendly cats providing food for each other's kittens have been documented many times. There is even one recorded instance from African wildcats. Perhaps there is something about some households which triggers cats into behaving as if there are kittens present, and so bringing food home for them to share. This idea is compatible with the theory put forward above: that cats regard their owners as superior cats.

SOCIALIZATION; HOW DO KITTENS LEARN TO ACCEPT PEOPLE?

Most mammals and birds come into the world with only a hazy view of what other members of their species look like. Such knowledge may be important immediately, if they are to recognize the mother that will take care of them. It will certainly be important later, when they need to avoid mating with members of the wrong species. Most cats must have at least a double identity, because they look to us for food, but to other cats for reproduction. This double (sometimes multiple) identity is not something that kittens are born with, but is a product of socialization.

The early ethologists were very interested in socialization, but most of the studies were carried out on birds, particularly waterfowl, where its effects are most striking. Ducklings and goslings become mobile soon after hatching, and must quickly form an attachment to their mother to avoid becoming separated from her. The process whereby this happens is called "imprinting". Between twelve and eighteen hours after hatching, mallard ducklings learn exactly what their mother looks like, and then follow her closely. As soon as this learning process is over, they become frightened of strange objects, so preventing further imprinting from taking place. The object that they imprint on to is not selected at random, however; it must approximate reasonably well in size and appearance to an adult duck. It is almost as if the duckling is provided with an imaginary sketch to which it adds relevant detail. If no such object is available, the sketch gradually simplifies, so that ducklings that never see an adult duck will eventually imprint on to an artificial object, such as a balloon. Most people will be familiar with pictures of the goslings that became imprinted to Konrad Lorenz, who won a Nobel Prize for his contributions to ethology.

The short duration of the imprinting period seems to be designed to ensure that only relevant information is learned. Too short, and the duckling might learn what its mother looks like from the side, but not from the back. Too long, and it might become imprinted on to another neighbouring female as well as to its mother, resulting in a dilemma if they swam off in opposite directions! The equivalent process in a mammal like the cat is more drawn-out, and its beginning and end are less well-defined, so it is known as "the sensitive phase", and the term "imprinting" is rarely applied.

Kittens have some sort of cat-like mental template that they use during socialization, but it is rather weak, and they will form attachments to any animated object that they experience repeatedly. Feral kittens that have been born in a well-hidden nest are unlikely to encounter any cat apart from their mother for the first few weeks of their lives, and by the time they encounter their first human they are likely to react with fear. Such kittens may never accept people, although very persistent contact with a human carer over a considerable period of time may eventually result in a reasonably well-socialized cat. Re-socialization can also be triggered by intense stress, probably through reactivation of the sensitive phase by the hormone noradrenaline. This has occurred when previously wild feral cats are incapacitated by injury or disease; such cats can become very attached to people who nurse them to recovery.

Until recently, it was assumed that the sensitive phase in kittens was the same as for puppies, that is, between about seven and fourteen weeks of age. Dr Eileen Karsh of Temple University, Philadelphia, showed that it actually occurs much earlier by giving kittens different degrees of handling by people. Kittens left with their mothers until they were about seven or fourteen weeks of age were equally unsociable, but those handled between two and six weeks old, or three and seven weeks old, were the most sociable. Thus the sensitive phase of the kitten lasts from about the end of the second week to the end of the seventh. Mildred Moelk has claimed that beneficial effects can result if kittens are first handled when they are only a few days old, and I have personally done this with all of the kittens born to my own cat Lucy. Certainly it should be performed in a gentle way so as not to distress the mother, but Lucy never objected unless one of the kittens cried out, whereupon we returned it to her immediately.

The amount and quality of the handling are also important. Eileen Karsh found that a typical kitten that had been handled for only fifteen minutes each day would, when older, approach its handler, head rub on her, and then move away. A kitten handled for over an hour a day would be more likely to climb up on her lap, purr, and either play or go to sleep, depending on its mood. The number and variety of people that the kitten encounters at this stage also affect its behaviour later in life. For example, there are many cats that behave in a much more outgoing way towards unfamiliar women than unfamiliar men. This may be partly accounted for by the similarity between men's low-pitched voices and the cat's growl, but such cats may not have been socialized to men when they were kittens.

The length of the sensitive phase – about six weeks compared to the mallard duck's six hours – means that kittens have time to socialize to cats, people, and other species such as dogs. All my own kittens have encountered my labrador at an early age; if they were old enough to hiss (this defensive vocalization appears in about the fourth week) they usually did that on the first one or two occasions, but they all rapidly socialized to him after that. Orphaned kittens that have been raised with puppies evidently regard them as good substitutes for their own siblings, and all will sleep together in a contented heap.

Since the sensitive phase is so critical to the bond between cats and people, it is likely to have been crucial to the domestication of the African wildcat. Reay Smithers' hand-reared females were evidently socialized both to him and to his dog, because both were regular recipients of their rubs. The duration of the sensitive phase in the African wildcat has not been measured, but it must be long enough, and the template broad enough, to permit socialization to both man and dog. It is tempting to speculate that the crucial change brought about by domestication was not the acceptance of man by kittens, but by mothers.

Most species, and wildcats seem to be no exception, are at their most defensive when they have newborn young. The same hormonal changes that permit female domestic cats to relax their wariness of one another and share a nest (*see Chapter 7*) may also relax their suspicions of humans. This would have allowed domestication and the beginnings of cat-cat social behaviour to develop side-by-side.

ARE SOME CATS NATURALLY MORE FRIENDLY TO PEOPLE THAN OTHERS?

In all of Eileen Karsh's studies of socialization, there was a considerable variety between kittens in the extent to which they responded to the handling regimes. Other workers have gone on to try to classify the "personalities" of cats, and to find out why they might vary. Dennis Turner has produced three categories: unfriendly cats, cats that need to be approached but are then friendly, and cats that are both friendly and outgoing. Dr Turner has also made a distinction between cats that prefer games and those that prefer to be stroked.

Characteristics such as boldness and nervousness are

strongly influenced by early experiences, and may persist throughout the life of the cat. However, socialization and other learning early on in life are not the only determinants of a cat's personality. Friendly mother and father cats tend to have friendly kittens, and this suggests that inherited factors play a part also. Friendly mothers could, in theory, influence their kittens in two distinct ways. First, they could pass on genes which help their kittens to socialize well with people. Second, they could influence their kittens' interactions with people directly. Kittens probably learn a great deal by copying their mother's lead, and if she is nervous or frightened when interacting with people, they may simply copy her. However, it is perfectly simple to arrange for a tom cat not to even see his kittens; since they cannot then copy his behaviour, he can only influence them through his genes. This lack of ambiguity is the reason why cat biologists have concentrated on the inheritance of behavioural traits from the father, rather than the mother. It has now been demonstrated several times that tom cats tend to produce kittens that are as friendly or unfriendly as they are themselves. Mothers must also tend to produce kittens that are as friendly or unfriendly as they are, although they will also influence their kittens' friendliness directly, through their own behaviour.

None of this work means that it will be possible to identify a "friendliness" gene for cats. Genes produce proteins, not behaviour, and the link between proteins and friendliness must be highly complex. Variations in friendliness presumably arise from small changes in the nervous system, and its responsiveness to external stimuli and hormone levels, but our current understanding of these systems is woefully inadequate. What these experiments have made us realize is that a cat's personality is partly dependent on its parents, and partly on its experiences.

WHAT WE DO TO CATS

Humans control the breeding of most domesticated animals. In some circumstances this control is almost total. The modern farming practice of artificial insemination allows small numbers of males to father huge numbers of offspring, producing highly uniform breeds. The popularity of champion male dogs as sires can lead to imbalances in the genetics of their breeds, and in

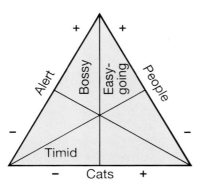

some countries, notably Sweden, restrictions have been placed on the number of times a male can be mated. In the case of cats, breeding is carefully arranged for the small percentage that belong to recognized breeds, but for the remaining 90 per cent or more of cats, that choice of sexual partner is often left to the cat. This is an unusually high proportion for a domesticated animal, and is one of the reasons why some biologists still classify the cat as a domestic captive animal. However, unrestricted breeding in the proximity of man is rarely desirable either from the cat's or our own points of view.

Given the cat's ability to survive and breed by scavenging food from humans and their garbage, it must have been necessary from the earliest times to exert some kind of population control. Cats are still regarded as vermin in some parts of the world, and the adults may be shot, poisoned or trapped. Others die in accidents or succumb to disease, with the result that feral cats usually do not survive beyond their third or fourth year. For pet cats, one traditional method of population control is to drown most or all of the kittens in each litter soon after birth. Such methods are not compatible with recent attitudes to the rights of animals, at least in Northern Europe and North America, and organizations that rescue unwanted cats are now widespread. Pet cats can sometimes be transferred straight from one household to another, but if a new home cannot be found immediately, they have to join other rescued cats, including ferals and those which need veterinary attention, in animal shelters.

For an animal as territorial as a cat, being forcibly moved to a new location must be a stressful experience. When shelters are crowded, the sight and sound of other cats nearby, possibly

THE "BEHAVIOURAL STYLES" OF CATS

Three separate studies of cat personalities have all come to similar conclusions, that there are three basic underlying factors that combine together to produce the cat's "behavioural style". These factors are shown on the sides of the triangle (i) how alert and generally active (+) or inactive (−) the cat is, (ii) whether it reacts to other cats calmly (+) or aggressively (−), and (iii) whether it tends to approach people spontaneously (+) or keep away from them (−). Three common types of cat result from combinations of these factors: the bossy cat, the timid cat and the easy-going cat.

even sharing the same pen, can only induce more stress. It is a tribute to the cat's resilience and adaptability that so many adjust reasonably quickly to shelter life. Attempts to escape usually die down after a few days, being replaced by a period of quiescence in which the cat may spend a large proportion of its time in hiding (*see page 215*).

Some shelters are able to provide long-term accommodation for cats that prove difficult to home. More economical use can be made of the space available if the cats can be housed in large groups. When a cat is moved into communal housing, it may exhibit the same signs of stress as it did when it was first rescued. These rarely last for more than a few weeks, however, and it appears that cats that are confined together for months or even years can form social affiliations even if they were initially hostile to one another. If the initial period of readjustment is successful, communal housing does appear to bring real benefits to the cats, as well as being more economical and convenient for those who look after them.

Anaesthesia and modern surgical techniques have allowed neutering of both males and females to become the main method of limiting the growth of the cat population. In many parts of Northern Europe and North America and elsewhere, it is now the accepted practice to have all pet cats neutered before puberty. Neutering is also increasingly used as a population control measure for feral cats (*see Chapter 7*). In some parts of the United Kingdom, neutering is so widespread that animal welfare organizations are reporting more demand for kittens then they can satisfy.

From the individual owner's point of view, the immediate benefits of neutering, castration of males in particular, have more to do with behaviour than with population control. As described in Chapter 7, the behaviour of unneutered male cats is largely incompatible with life in a human household, although their large size and broad head and shoulders give them an appeal that is quite distinct from that of the slender female. Towards the end of their first year, toms begin to enlarge their home ranges, with the intention of locating unneutered females. They also begin to scent-mark by urine-spraying, which may initially go unnoticed if it occurs out of doors, but is hard to mistake indoors, particularly as the urine begins to take on its characteristic and pungent "tom-catty" odour. Fights with other neighbourhood tom cats become more and more frequent, and more serious, resulting in torn ears and abscesses in puncture-wounds.

Castration before puberty usually prevents these habits from developing. Surprisingly, castration after puberty is almost as successful; substantial reductions in the amount of spraying and fighting are often reported even when the tom is neutered when two or more years old. This is in direct contrast to the limited effectiveness of castration for reducing indoor urine-marking and aggression in male dogs. Roaming, on the other hand, does not appear to be reliably reduced by castration. In one study carried out in Manchester, England, the home ranges of cats neutered at a given age were the same as those of un-neutered males of that age. In other words, as males get older, they enlarge their ranges; castration prevents any further in-crease, but the habit of roaming over a particular area is not broken.

Spraying is observed in about one-third of castrated males, but because it usually occurs out of doors, and the urine is much less pungent than that of an entire tom, it does not often cause an offence. Although they are unable to breed, the behaviour of neutered toms is affected to a remarkable extent by the sex of other cats in the household. Males living with females are about twice as likely to fight and spray as those living with other males.

Apart from the period of oestrus, the behavioural effects of neutering are less for females than they are for males. Neutered and unneutered females that are not in season have similar home-range sizes, which is hardly surprising as both will be determined by the availability and distribution of food, rather than potential mates (see Chapter 7). If there is a shortage of males in the area, a female in season may roam more widely than usual, in search of a mate. Between seasons, females behave in much the same way whether or not they have been neutered. Only about 10 per cent of neutered females spray, but fighting is about equally common in neutered males and neutered females.

From the point of view of the pet-owner, neutering is almost always beneficial. Neutered cats live longer and healthier lives, and their relationship with their owner is not interrupted by the demands of mating and reproduction.

One of the beneficial effects of neutering feral cats: contrast the condition of Sid soon after neutering (above) and a year later (opposite).

BEHAVIOUR OF RESCUED CATS

Three students at Southampton University, Debby Smith, Katie Durman and David Roy, have made studies of the way cats behave when they are confined in an animal shelter. They measured the way that the cats' behaviour changes depending on how long they stay in the shelter, and how their environment might be improved to reduce the stress of confinement.

When they first arrive at a shelter, it is usual for cats to be isolated for a time if there is any risk that they might be carrying a contagious disease. However, pressure of space often means that new healthy cats have to be put in a pen with one or two others.

We studied groups of between four and seven cats housed together. For the first four days or so after they joined such a group, new cats would attempt to escape by climbing up or biting the bars of the door, or they might sit by the door and miaow. They were initially very wary of the other cats, hissing and growling at them, adopting defensive postures and moving away whenever possible. Yet towards the end of their first week in the shelter, their behaviour would usually change dramatically. On average, escape attempts and vocalizations diminished to about 10 per cent of their initial rate, indicating that the first acute stress was over.

However, some other measurements that we made suggested that many had simply changed to a more passive strategy for coping with stress. The amount of time that the new cats spent hiding declined slowly, and still averaged over a quarter of the day in the fourth week. Although the cats were offered individual bowls of food, a minority would wait until all the other cats had fed before eating themselves, though this habit had largely disappeared by the fourth week. We also had the impression that every new introduction caused all the other cats in the pen to become temporarily more wary of one another.

We also observed marked changes in the behaviour of long-stay cats kept in larger groups, up to twenty in pens with access to outdoor runs. When first introduced into these groups, the cats would exhibit some of the same disturbances of behaviour as they had done when first confined. They would frequently refuse meals, and many would miaow repeatedly, or attempt to escape by climbing the mesh walls of their run. They kept their distance from all the other cats, and spent a large proportion of their time alert, rarely sleeping during the day, and always paused to carefully check if a pen was occupied before entering it.

However, within a month or so all of these patterns of behaviour had disappeared or at least decreased substantially, indicating that stress had subsided. The majority of the cats that had been in the shelter for over a year had developed social bonds with other long-stay cats; they frequently rested in contact with their preferred partners, and were hardly ever aggressive (see Chapter 7 for a more detailed description of their social structure).

Some of the runs already contained objects such as chairs and logs, and it was evident that the cats preferred to rest on these rather than on the ground, and often used them as the bars of the door, or they might sit by the door and vantage-points. We tried out a number of different specially-built wooden structures to see how they were used by the cats. Some cats used the top surfaces, others preferred the security provided by enclosed areas beneath. When we covered parts of the tops of the structures with other materials, such as carpet, plastic and aluminium, most of the cats opted to stay on the wooden sur-faces that were still exposed. However, the choice of enclosed areas was hardly influenced by the type of surface; the parts of the pen that could be surveyed from them seemed to be the main factor in deciding whether or not they would be occupied by a cat.

TERRITORIAL BEHAVIOUR OF PET CATS

Because it is fed there, a pet cat's territory is centred on its owner's house. If there are many other cats living nearby, some cats may encounter aggression as soon as they set foot out of doors. More seriously, cat-flaps not only allow the resident cat out, but also permit other cats to come in to steal food. If this occurs regularly, the resident cat may feel threatened and be-havioural problems, such as indoor urination and defaecation, will result.

By the time my male cat Splodge was eighteen months old, he had begun to be absent from the house for hours at a time, so I attached a minute radio-transmitter to his collar, and used this to locate him every few hours for three weeks. As well as resting in my garden, I discovered that he had two favourite hunting areas on the edge of the park nearby (see map). In order to reach them, he had to pass through the territories of other male cats, either an eight-year old black-and-white moggie, or a five-year old Persian. Before venturing on either of these journeys, he would look round carefully, and then move quickly until he had disappeared into cover.

The neutered female that lived across the road was able to roam much more freely, presumably because she was the only female in the area. Her home range overlapped with those of Splodge and also the Persian, and she was never seen to be attacked by any of the other cats, although Splodge frequently had to run for his cat-flap with a male in hot pursuit.

(Above) Max, a rescued feral male, unlikely ever to find an owner. Social contact with other cats in the shelter can be beneficial. (Right) The company of a cat can provide benefits to health as well as pleasure.

WHAT CATS DO FOR US

A one-sided relationship is unlikely to flourish; for cat-keeping to have lasted for so long, benefits must have been mutual. Cats are now distributed all over the world, and the human-cat relationship is probably stronger and more widespread now than it has ever been before. We give cats food, shelter and company,

although increasingly we are taking away from them their right to breed when and where they choose. In some places the cats still fulfil their traditional practical role, but in modern cities the benefits to humans must be purely psychological.

Part of the cat's success stems from its abilities as a controller of rodent pests. This has provided a practical reason for people to keep cats. It has also probably provided many cat-lovers with an excuse for keeping a pet cat in places or times where cats were unpopular. However, it is a tribute to the cat's adaptability and broad appeal that its numbers are continuing to increase in areas where agrochemical methods of pest control have displaced them from their traditional role. Why this should be so, and for that matter why a minority of people have a horror of cats, is worth a book in itself. As a biologist, it particularly interests me how cats affect the success of their hosts, people. Do they take from us, without giving anything in return, or do they enhance our lives by enriching our culture, improving our relationships with others, or even making us healthier?

The last of these has received some attention recently, mostly as a spin-off from more detailed studies of the impact of dogs on human health. It is reasonable to assume that the regular exercising of a dog should help to counteract the unhealthy aspects of the largely sedentary life of modern man, and several scientific studies have demonstrated this. Some of the other health benefits ascribed to dogs might also apply to cats. For example, stroking a (familiar) dog lowers one's blood pressure, and there is no reason to suppose that this should not be equally true of cats. Professor Erika Friedmann has demonstrated that pets, including cats, significantly improve recovery after a heart attack, over and above the simple benefits brought about by exercising a dog. A recent study by Warwick Anderson and others in Australia has shown that cat owners who took preventative cardiac checkups had lower cholesterol levels, lower triglycerides and lower systolic blood pressure than similar people who did not own cats.

Dr James Serpell, at Cambridge University, has also shown that people's health improves when they acquire a new cat. He conducted a survey of twenty-four families who had obtained a cat from an animal shelter, and had not kept a cat or a dog during the previous year. The owners reported fewer minor health

Cat symbols

P Persian

C Black and white crossbreed

♂ Splodge

♀ Female

(Left) The areas used regularly by two young cats. Two older cats lived in adjacent houses, and the young male, Splodge, tended to choose places where he could avoid them (see page 217).

problems after one month of acquiring the cat, and their general health was distinctly improved five months later. By ten months after the new cat's arrival, the improvements were no longer reported, but presumably cats continue to exert a subconscious effect for longer than this, or the health benefits described above cannot be explained.

Cats are resilient animals, and should continue to share the human environment for as far into the future as we can see. The more that biologists find out about them, the more complex and mysterious they seem to become. For my own part, trying to understand why they do the things they do has been, and will continue to be, an endless source of fascination. Hopefully this book will have helped to explain some of the things that your cat does, but certainly not everything. That is part of their charm.

Index